George
Westinghouse

Young Inventor

Illustrated by Gray Morrow

George
Westinghouse

Young Inventor

By *Montrew Dunham*

THE **BOBBS-MERRILL** COMPANY, INC.
A SUBSIDIARY OF HOWARD W. SAMS & CO., INC.
Publishers • INDIANAPOLIS • NEW YORK

To Della Darling

Illustrations

Contents

Books by Montrew Dunham

GEORGE WESTINGHOUSE: YOUNG INVENTOR
OLIVER WENDELL HOLMES, JR.: BOY OF JUSTICE

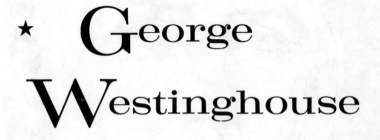

★ George Westinghouse

Young Inventor

INDIANS

POCAHONTAS, *Seymour*
PONTIAC, *Peckham*
SACAGAWEA, *Seymour*
SEQUOYAH, *Snow*
SITTING BULL, *Stevenson*
SQUANTO, *Stevenson*
TECUMSEH, *Stevenson*

NAVAL HEROES

DAVID FARRAGUT, *Long*
GEORGE DEWEY, *Long*
JOHN PAUL JONES, *Snow*
MATTHEW CALBRAITH PERRY, *Scharbach*
OLIVER HAZARD PERRY, *Long*
RAPHAEL SEMMES, *Snow*
STEPHEN DECATUR, *Smith*

NOTED WIVES and MOTHERS

ABIGAIL ADAMS, *Wagoner*
DOLLY MADISON, *Monsell*
JESSIE FREMONT, *Wagoner*
MARTHA WASHINGTON, *Wagoner*
MARY TODD LINCOLN, *Wilkie*
NANCY HANKS, *Stevenson*
RACHEL JACKSON, *Covan*

SCIENTISTS and INVENTORS

ALBERT EINSTEIN, *Hammontree*
ALECK BELL, *Widdemer*
CYRUS MCCORMICK, *Dobler*
ELI WHITNEY, *Snow*
ELIAS HOWE, *Corcoran*
ELIZABETH BLACKWELL, *Henry*
GAIL BORDEN, *Paradis*
GEORGE CARVER, *Stevenson*
GEORGE EASTMAN, *Henry*
GEORGE PULLMAN, *Myers*
GEORGE WESTINGHOUSE, *Dunham*
HENRY FORD, *Aird and Ruddiman*
JOHN AUDUBON, *Mason*
JOHN BURROUGHS, *Frisbee*
JOHN DEERE, *Bare*
LUTHER BURBANK, *Burt*
MARIA MITCHELL, *Melin*
ROBERT FULTON, *Henry*
SAMUEL MORSE, *Snow*
TOM EDISON, *Guthridge*
WALTER REED, *Higgins*

WILBUR AND ORVILLE WRIGHT, *Stevenson*
WILL AND CHARLIE MAYO, *Hammontree*

SOCIAL and CIVIC LEADERS

BETSY ROSS, *Weil*
BOOKER T. WASHINGTON, *Stevenson*
CLARA BARTON, *Stevenson*
DAN BEARD, *Mason*
DOROTHEA DIX, *Melin*
FRANCES WILLARD, *Mason*
J. STERLING MORTON, *Moore*
JANE ADDAMS, *Wagoner*
JULIA WARD HOWE, *Wagoner*
JULIETTE LOW, *Higgins*
LILIUOKALANI, *Newman*
LUCRETIA MOTT, *Burnett*
MOLLY PITCHER, *Stevenson*
OLIVER WENDELL HOLMES, JR., *Dunham*
SUSAN ANTHONY, *Monsell*

SOLDIERS

ANTHONY WAYNE, *Stevenson*
BEDFORD FORREST, *Parks*
DAN MORGAN, *Bryant*
ETHAN ALLEN, *Winders*
FRANCIS MARION, *Steele*
GEORGE CUSTER, *Stevenson*
ISRAEL PUTNAM, *Stevenson*
JEB STUART, *Winders*
NATHANAEL GREENE, *Peckham*
ROBERT E. LEE, *Monsell*
SAM HOUSTON, *Stevenson*
TOM JACKSON, *Monsell*
U. S. GRANT, *Stevenson*
WILLIAM HENRY HARRISON, *Peckham*
ZACK TAYLOR, *Wilkie*

STATESMEN

ABE LINCOLN, *Stevenson*
ANDY JACKSON, *Stevenson*
DAN WEBSTER, *Smith*
FRANKLIN ROOSEVELT, *Weil*
HENRY CLAY, *Monsell*
JAMES MONROE, *Widdemer*
JEFF DAVIS, *de Grummond and Delaune*
JOHN F. KENNEDY, *Frisbee*
JOHN MARSHALL, *Monsell*
TEDDY ROOSEVELT, *Parks*
WOODROW WILSON, *Monsell*

Time for School

GEORGE FELT warm and good as he pumped the water into the horse trough. The cold clear water gushed from the pump. George stopped pumping and leaned on the handle as he breathed deeply of the fresh sweet April air. The sunshine filled the valley all around him. Spring was so wonderful after the long cold winter.

It was a lovely morning in the spring of 1854 in Central Bridge, New York, and George Westinghouse was seven years old.

George ran to the near-by barn to let his father's horse Molly out into the barnlot. The horse raised her head with a whinny and trotted out into the sunshine. He ran and patted the horse on her soft nose. "Do you like spring too?"

His winter underwear felt scratchy and hot as he hopped and skipped to the house for breakfast. When he ran through the back door into the kitchen, he asked, "Ma, can I take off my long underwear?"

His mother was standing by the big black cookstove. She turned to look over her shoulder. She smiled and looked out of the corner of her eyes. "George! You know it's not time for that yet! There'll be more chilly weather."

"But, Ma—at least, would you cut off the sleeves?" George begged.

Mother smiled and shook her head. "Come now for your buckwheat cakes."

"Yes, Mam!" George went to the stove to look at the steaming cakes on the hot griddle. "Do they smell good!" He reached to the back of the stove to stir the batter in the pitcher.

12

"George, keep your hands out of that!" Mother scolded. "Now get to the table. Your brothers are almost finished."

George grinned. "Ma, when did you make the batter for the buckwheat cakes?"

Mother placed a plate heaped high with a stack of steaming buckwheat cakes before George. "Last night, after you were in bed."

"You should have seen it this morning!" said Albert. "The batter raised so, it was running out of the pitcher. Ma really had to stir it down."

George put a chunk of freshly churned butter on the stack. As it melted over the sides, he poured rich brown maple syrup over the cakes. Then he ate as fast as he could. The cakes tasted so good, he just couldn't eat them fast enough!

"Do you want some more cakes, George?" Mother asked, pouring batter on the griddle.

George's mouth was so full, he had to gulp to swallow so that he could answer his mother.

"I sure do, Ma!" Then he popped another syrupy bite into his mouth.

"I declare, George," Mother laughed, "though you are only seven, you can eat as much as your big brothers!"

"George is eating more than I can! And I'm thirteen, going on fourteen!" John exclaimed.

George started to answer John that he was seven and a half, not just seven, but his mouth was too full. He just shrugged his shoulders and kept on eating.

"Come on Albert, let's go to school," said John. "We don't want to be late."

Albert pushed his chair back and followed John to the door. "You had better come too, George. You can't sit there eating all day!"

"You must leave for school, George, if you are to get there on time," chided his mother.

George planted a sticky kiss on his Mother's cheek and ran after his brothers.

14

"Your sister Mary is already on her way," Mrs. Westinghouse said. "You must hurry!"

"Albert, wait for me," he called as he skipped down the path to the road. He slowed to a walk when he came to the muddy road. His feet made such gooshy sounds as he walked through the sticky mud. When he placed one foot down solidly, it squooshed, and then as he slowly picked up the other foot, the mud squished. So he walked very slowly and enjoyed the muddy sounds. He took a deep breath to feel the delicious freshness of the moist spring air.

The soft spring breeze ruffled George's fair hair. The sky was blue and the grass was bright green. George felt so good. The world was exciting! He loved the fields and hills, the springtime rushing water of the Schoharie River, and the swift flow of the Cobleskill Creek, but most of all he liked the shop where his father built threshing machines.

George stopped to look up at the tall tree beside him. Its branches were covered with the buds of new leaves. He could almost see the leaves unfolding!

George started to think of something else, something he would like to do. He didn't see his brothers coming back for him. Then suddenly he was lifted off the ground.

John and Albert each grabbed one of his arms and swung him off his feet. "It's time for school, little boy. You'd better be on your way," chanted John in a singsong voice.

"Leave me alone!" demanded George as he flounced around between them.

"All right," said John, "but you had better hurry or you will be late." The two big boys let go of his arms and he dropped to the ground.

George's face was red, and his eyebrows drew down into a frown. It made him feel cross to be

16

treated like a baby. He pulled some pieces of wood and some pins out of his pocket.

"What are you going to do with that junk?" laughed Albert.

"I'm going to make a machine go round and round." George fitted two sticks together.

John shook his head. "Oh George," he laughed, "you'll never make anything out of that junk!"

A deep line creased between George's eyebrows. His lower lip stuck out with determination as he retorted, "I will, too!"

The big boys laughed and ran on their way to school. George looked after his brothers. He pressed his mouth together in a tight line. He was thinking, "I'll show them!" when someone came up behind him.

"Did you see the bird?" asked a familiar voice. George looked around to see his friend Jacob walking up beside him.

"Be still and listen!" Jacob whispered.

17

George stood still and listened as hard as he could. Then he heard the sound of a bird's happy song. He looked up into the tree, but he couldn't see any birds. Jacob crept around the tree, trying to follow the sound of the bird. George tiptoed softly behind. Then they saw!

In a bush in the back of the yard sat the bird, singing its joyous song of spring. The boys, careful to make no noise, walked slowly toward the bush, but the bird flew away.

Jacob and George stopped and looked at each other and laughed with the delight of spring.

"What are those?" asked Jacob as he noticed the sticks which George was holding tightly.

George's thoughts quickly returned to his bits of wood and pins. "Oh," he answered, "I must get this machine put together."

"Machine?" Jacob asked.

George threw off his coat and flung it on the ground. He knelt down and laid his sticks in order on top of his coat. "I'm going to put these together, and the sticks will go round and round to make a machine." He reached into his coat pocket for some pins and his knife. His blue eyes were serious as his stubby fingers arranged the sticks and placed each pin through the proper place. Then he drew his mouth down tightly as he bent the pin into place.

"Bong! Bong! Bong!" The clear sound of the school bell rang through the valley to remind all the pupils of the time for school.

"George! There's the school bell . . ." Jacob tugged at George's shirt sleeve. "We must go!"

George didn't lift his head. He opened his knife and carefully whittled a piece of wood.

Again through the valley came the rhythmic bonging of the school bell, calling all the tardy pupils to school.

"I'm going!" Jacob started to run to the road. "You'd better come, George!"

George didn't hear him leave. He whittled first on one piece of wood and then on another. He fitted two pieces together and then took them apart to carve some more until the parts fitted. Then he put the two together carefully and fastened them with a pin.

Finally George finished his little machine. He turned one stick and the others turned in motion just as he hoped they would!

Still on his knees he straightened his back, and he slowly turned the little handle which made the other stick go. George smiled. He had finished his machine just right, and it worked!

His shoulders felt hot with the warmth of the golden sunshine. He looked up. The day was bright and the sun was high in the sky. The bird was gone. The grass was no longer moist with morning dew. Somehow a great deal of time had slipped away from him.

He stood up slowly and looked down the road toward school. The valley was quiet, and there was no sound of the school bell.

"Oh, my!" George said to himself. "Oh my! It's too late to go to school now."

He picked up his cap from the ground and jammed it on his head. He threw his coat over his shoulder. He scowled a little. He knew he should have gone to school. He picked up his machine. He had finished his work, though, and he did have to get it finished. He smiled . . . and started to walk . . . and then he skipped a little.

He knew what he would do! He would go to his father's shop. It was always such fun to see the men building threshing machines.

He hesitated a moment. His father would be angry with him because he hadn't gone to school. He almost stopped. Then he walked along slowly, dragging the toes of his boots, one after the other, through the crusty mud.

He thought about the big thresher his father and the men were building for Farmer Vrooman. He wanted to see how much they had done. He started to walk a little faster. After all, it was too late to go to school now. He might just as well go to the shop.

He ran down the road to the shop. The doors were open, and the sunlight streamed in through the doors and windows onto the huge machine in the middle of the floor.

The thresher looked so large. There were two men working on it. Mr. Westinghouse looked around from his work to see George standing in the doorway and walked over to his son.

"Oh," he said, "what have we here?"

George's shoulders raised as he took a deep breath. He tried to stiffen his courage.

"George, what are you doing here at this time of day?" Mr. Westinghouse looked very serious, but his voice was quiet and calm.

George didn't know what to say! His face felt a little warm. He looked up into his father's eyes. Then he shrugged a little. He opened his mouth, but he couldn't say anything.

"Well . . ." Father looked very stern.

He wrinkled his face and bit his lips a little. He looked at the floor and then back at Father. "Pa, I was late . . . and . . ."

"You started to school with your brothers . . . were they late?" Father asked quietly.

George took his cap off and rubbed his forehead on his sleeve. He still had his machine of sticks and pins in his other hand. "No sir."

"What is this?" Father asked as he pointed to George's machine.

George sighed. He never quite knew how to tell his father about his work. He started slowly, "Well you see, I just had to finish this. It's a . . ."

Mr. Westinghouse frowned. "George, you are expected to go to school, and you must go!"

George turned the little stick. "Look, Pa, it works! I had to make it work!"

His father wasn't watching. He placed his hands on George's shoulders. "Son, it is important! You must go to school to learn. You cannot stay home to make toys. Do you understand, George?"

George felt sad as he answered his father. "Yes, Pa, I understand," but he didn't really.

The Threshing Machine

GEORGE WENT to school each day as his father said he should. When the morning school bell rang George trudged down the road to the small schoolhouse. He sat at his desk and looked out the window at the big trees with their green leaves stirring in the wind. He turned around to look at his big brothers sitting in the back of the schoolroom. Albert and John were working diligently at their arithmetic.

George sighed and looked back at his slate on his desk. He picked up his slate pencil and started to study spelling. His thoughts wandered to the sticks and pins in his desk.

He wished he could have time to do his work! He put his hand into the desk to see if all the sticks and pins were still there. Then he put his elbows on his desk and rested his chin in his hands. He was so tired of school.

The day was long and tiresome, but at last the teacher rang the bell that told the pupils school was over for the day.

George jammed his books and slate into his desk and rushed through the aisle to the door. He wanted to get out into the sunshine. He leaped and ran with joy. He could hardly run fast enough to his father's shop to see how the big thresher was coming along.

Piece by piece the threshing machine was being put together. It was wonderful how the men knew what to do next. Each day George could see that the machine was closer to being finished.

He stood and admired the enormous machine. He watched Mr. Long work on a wheel.

"How do you know what to do next?" George
marveled.

Mr. Long looked at the boy and smiled. "Your
pa tells us."

"But how does he know?" George asked the workman, who was laying down his tools.

Mr. Long stood up slowly and stretched his legs. His eyes crinkled as he smiled at George. "Well, I'll tell you. Your pa knows about making farm machinery. He makes and plans, and we follow what he has shown us to do. Your pa has even invented some of these parts in the thresher and has patents on them."

"Patents?" George didn't understand.

"Your pa figured out a new part to make the thresher work better, so he got a patent on it. This is his own invention." Mr. Long pointed to a part in the machine.

George frowned a little as he tried to understand. "What is a patent?"

Mr. Long looked down at George's wide blue eyes. "Well, George, when a man invents something new, he can send a record of his invention to Washington. Then he is given a patent, which shows that this invention was his, and that it is his right alone to manufacture it or to sell it to other men."

"Can't other people build threshers?"

"Sure they can. Lots of companies build threshers," Mr. Long explained. "But if these companies want to use this new part which makes the thresher work better than any other one, they have to get permission from your pa."

George smiled. "Has Pa ever invented any other things before he started to make this thresher? Did he ever get any other patents?"

"Oh yes, he's thought up many ways to help in building farm machinery. He has three or four patents!" Mr. Long sighed and knelt down again to his work. "Now you go on. I must get busy again if we're to have this thresher ready for Farmer Vrooman when the wheat is ripe. He won't have any use for the machine unless it's ready to use at the right time."

The last day of school finally came, and not too long after that the threshing machine was finished and ready to be used. It was completed just at the right time, because the wheat was golden ripe and ready to be threshed.

The July evening was hot and still. The summer sun was still shining brightly as the Westinghouse family gathered around the supper table.

Father looked very pleasant as he announced, "The thresher is to be taken to the Vrooman place tomorrow for the threshing."

"Oh Pa! Can we go too?" asked eleven-year-old Albert. "We want to see how it works!"

"Yes, Albert. I want you, John and Jay to go along to help."

George's heart pounded. He could feel the thuds clear up in his throat. How wonderful! He could hardly wait to see the threshing machine really work.

31

As he crawled into bed George could think of nothing else. The night was hot. A slight breeze drifted through the open windows. The large pale moon was just coming up in the eastern sky. George thought of the enormous piece of machinery in the shop. How could they ever pull it clear to Vrooman's farm? Then he frowned to himself. What was it Pa had said when Albert had asked if the boys could go along. His father's words went through his thoughts clearly. "Yes, Albert, I want you, John and Jay to go along to help!" George sat straight up in bed. Pa hadn't said he could go! Oh! Wouldn't it be awful if he couldn't!

Morning came. The night and sleep had taken away some of his concern that he couldn't go. Surely he could!

He jumped into his clothes. He buttoned his shirt as he ran down stairs. He just couldn't get to the shop fast enough!

"George! Come for breakfast," Mother called.

"Oh Ma. I haven't time to eat!" George was in a great hurry to get to the shop.

"You haven't time to eat!" Mother raised her eyebrows. "This has never happened before."

George grinned. "Well, maybe I will stop for a little something since I'm going to work hard." His stomach did feel very empty, and Father had said he wanted the boys to help.

Mother smiled as she watched George gulp down his food. "All right, George, go on. I'll be along in a little while."

George was surprised. "Oh, are you coming to see the threshing too, Ma?"

"I wouldn't think of missing it," his mother replied. "This is an important day."

George hesitated a minute. "Oh Ma." He had an awful thought. "What if it doesn't work!"

"Of course it will work," Mother said confidently. "Your father's machines always work."

As George ran to the shop he could see the crowd that had gathered to watch. George darted among the folks standing about. Everyone in Central Bridge was here! What an exciting time! How proud George was of his father!

Farmer Vrooman and his hired man were hitching the team of heavy draft horses to the front of the threshing machine. Father looked so calm! His voice was even and low as he showed how the horses should be hitched.

"George, stand back! You'll get in the way!" George looked up and saw that he was standing beside his oldest brother Jay.

"I want to see!" He stood on tiptoe so that he could see what was being done.

The big sweating horses obeyed perfectly as they were backed and then led forward and back again into the proper place.

Farmer Vrooman and Father were talking, but George couldn't hear what they were saying.

34

"Stand back, folks," Mr. Westinghouse spoke out clearly, "we're bringing her out."

The crowd drew back from the shop onto the road. George saw his mother standing at the edge of the group.

The hired man tugged at the reins lightly. "Giddap." Together the team pulled easily but firmly, and slowly the threshing machine drew out into full view. 1747242

"Well, there she is!" said Farmer Vrooman proudly. "Isn't she a beauty!"

The men walked around the thresher, talking to each other about how this machine would work. The ladies lifted their long skirts a bit as they walked over the dusty road. They were interested in the excitement of the day, but they preferred to talk to each other instead of looking at new machinery.

"Well, fellows, I'm sorry to stop you from looking this over, but we have a day's work ahead of us." Mr. Vrooman turned to Father. "Shall I take her on?"

"Yes, start on, and I'll be right behind you in the wagon," answered Mr. Westinghouse.

Pa looked around. "Come on, boys." Jay climbed up into the wagon and Albert came running from up front by the horses. "John, come on! We're leaving right now."

The excitement was over! George felt a deep thumping inside his chest. His brothers were going to the threshing, but he had to stay home like a baby! His throat felt hot and dry, and he lifted his eyebrows up high. He was afraid the tears in his eyes would overflow and people would think he was crying!

As Mr. Westinghouse looked about him for his son John, his gaze rested on George. The little boy was standing straight and tall, but his blue eyes looked so moist, and his disappointment was mirrored on his face.

"George, hurry, or you'll be left!"

George could scarcely believe what he heard. "Yes sir!" he answered as he scrambled into the wagon as fast as he could.

The threshing machine, drawn by the strong team, lumbered down the road. Mr. Westinghouse and his sons followed in their wagon. Pa stopped the horses as soon as they turned into the lane at the Vrooman farm. George and his brothers leaped out of the wagon. The team pulled the thresher onto the field by the barn lot.

"Whoa!" called Mr. Vrooman. "Is this right?"

"That's just fine," George's father answered. "Adam Long and I will get the machine rigged up while the rest of you do your work."

"Shall the cradlers start cutting the wheat?" Farmer Vrooman asked.

"The thresher will be ready for the wheat by the time they've cradled a wagon load," Mr. Westinghouse assured him.

37

"Jacob!" George cried as he saw his friend running toward him.

"Hi George. I got to come with my pa, too," Jacob answered. "I'm going to be water boy."

Mr. Westinghouse heard Jacob. "George, I thought you could help by being a water boy too. The men get very thirsty on a hot day."

George grinned. "Come on Jacob. Let's get the buckets and dippers." It was wonderful to be out here with all the men, instead of staying home like a baby.

The boys stood and watched as George's father and Adam Long hooked up the belt to the wheels. Pa and Adam then led the horse up on the tread-mill and harnessed her.

"We're set here!" called Mr. Westinghouse.

"We'll be there with a load of wheat shortly!" answered Farmer Vrooman.

The big field of ripe wheat dipped and waved like a golden sea. The cradlers were cutting a

38

neat strip at one edge of the field, and the binders behind them were catching the bundles of wheat and tying them. The bundles were thrown into a wagon, and as soon as the wagon was filled, it was pulled over to the threshing machine. The wheat was fed into the hopper, and the thresher separated the grain from the straw and chaff.

"George!" Father saw the two boys standing behind him. "You and Jacob had better go to your task of getting water now."

"All right, Pa!" George grabbed Jacob's hand, and the two ran to the pump.

THE WATER BOYS

George and Jacob took turns pumping the water at the pump up by the house. They pumped until the water spurted cold and clear into their bucket. They watched the farm women preparing the dinner table for the threshers. The table had been set up near the pump, and the women were laying the cloth and setting places for all the hard-working farm men.

"Come on, George." Jacob and George each took hold of a side of the bucket handle. Carrying the heavy bucket between them, they went all the way out to the field. They came up to Peter Shultz, who was cutting the wheat with his mighty cradle. Mr. Shultz put his cradle down and mopped his forehead.

"That looks mighty good," he said. He took the dipper from the side of the pail and dipped it in the cool water. As he thirstily drank the water down, little streams of water spilled down the sides of the dipper to drop down his beard. "Ah, that was good!" He dipped another dipper of water and poured it over his head. Then he put his hat back on.

Jacob and George went from man to man until their water bucket was empty. Then they refilled it at the pump and started their rounds again. Each time they went past the threshing machine, George would stop and put the bucket down. He was interested in how the steady plodding walk of the horse on the treadmill made the wheels go round and turn the machinery in the thresher to separate the grain from the straw.

It was hard for Jacob to understand how the machine worked. "How did your father know how to make this machine?" he asked George. "Did he see a machine somewhere like it?"

"Pa knows about these things. He even invented some of the parts on it."

George and Jacob were both glad when the dinner bell rang out from the house. George started to run at the first sound. "Wait," called Jacob. "Come get the bucket!"

George grabbed his side of the bucket and the two boys ran to the house, swinging the empty bucket between them.

The long table by the pump was loaded with steaming dishes of good food. Mrs. Vrooman was at the bell post pulling on the leather thong to ring the dinner bell so loud and clear it could be heard in the fields.

"Well, look who is here first!" laughed Jacob's mother. "The two hardest-working threshers!"

42

The other women, who were waiting to serve the threshers' table, laughed.

"That's as it should be," said Mrs. Vrooman. "You boys come over to this table." She pointed to a smaller table set for the children.

By this time the hot tired men were coming up from the field. They went to the pump and washed their faces and hands with loud splashing. It was exciting to hear the noise of all the loud talking and laughing.

George and Jacob loaded their plates from all the dishes of good food. They shoveled the food to their mouths just as fast as they could. It tasted so good, and they were both very hungry. George stopped long enough to take a thick slice of freshly baked bread and spread it thick with soft, freshly churned butter.

The men at the big table ate just as heartily and with as much gusto as the boys. The dishes were passed and refilled by the women.

43

The coffee cups were filled, emptied, and filled again. Then the meal was topped off by the cakes and pies which each of the farm women had baked that morning for the threshers.

The men leaned back in their chairs to talk as they rested. "How quickly that field is being turned into grain in the barn and strawstacks!" marveled Farmer Baum. The farmers were all surprised at how fast the work was going with the new machine to help.

Soon the men went back to the field again to finish the work of threshing.

Jacob and George carried water to the field and brought the empty bucket back to the pump. The bucket grew heavier with each trip. The day was nearly over when George said wearily, "Jacob, let's rest our feet a little."

Jacob just as wearily agreed. "Let's go on the other side of the new straw stack. It's shady there, and as cool as anywhere."

The boys sat down and the bucket rolled over at their feet. George stretched his legs and wiggled his toes. He stretched his arms and leaned his head back on the fresh sweet-smelling straw. They talked a little, but soon both boys were fast asleep.

The first thing George heard was his father calling him. Mr. Westinghouse shook his son gently. "It was a big day, wasn't it, son?"

George jumped to his feet. Then he rubbed his eyes. The sun was almost down, and the land was covered with the purplish-gray dusk of nightfall. He hadn't meant to go to sleep! "Yes sir. It was a big day!"

A New Home

Father often had to make trips to Schenectady to get metal parts to use on his farm machinery. His last trip was in the fall of 1855.

The afternoon he returned, George's mother and the big boys were putting the sauerkraut down in a big barrel. This year George got to help too. The hired man had brought a load of tight, crisp cabbage heads and stacked them outside the summer kitchen. George and Albert peeled off the coarse outer leaves and brought the cabbage heads inside to the cutter. Jay and John, and sometimes even Mary were cutting the cabbage. They would slide the head of cabbage back and forth over a wooden board with a stationary knife in it, to shred the cabbage.

Mother stayed by the barrel where the freshly-cut cabbage was placed in layers. As soon as there was a full pan of shredded cabbage Mary would take it to Mother. Ma would put it in the barrel and sprinkle it generously with salt. Then she could tamp it down gently with a wooden masher. The barrel was large, and it did not fill up very fast.

George took a load of cabbage heads to the cutters. Then he went to see how fast the big barrel was filling up. Little two-year-old Herman toddled along behind him.

George reached down into the barrel and pulled out a slice of cabbage heart and laid it on his tongue. His mouth watered! It was good!

"Here, none of that!" Mother scolded. "With all of you dipping into the barrel, we'll never get enough cabbage for kraut!"

Six-year-old Elizabeth stopped and watched George. Her eyes were bright, and her cheeks dimpled with pleasure as she watched George snitch his bite of juicy salted cabbage. "I want some!" she cried as she skipped over to the kraut barrel. Before her mother could stop her, she reached in and pulled out a handful of freshly crushed cabbage. As she ate it though, she made a wry face at its tangy salty flavor.

"Ma," George asked, "how long before it's really kraut?"

"As soon as we get all the cabbage cut and put down into the barrel, salted and stamped down," his mother answered, "we'll put a lid on the barrel and then leave it to work."

"What do you mean, work?" George interrupted. "Cabbage doesn't work, does it?"

"The cabbage ferments and becomes sauerkraut." Mother finished her sentence as she stood up to see how much cabbage was left to be cut.

48

"Now back to work, George. It looks as if we'll have a big barrel of kraut when we're finished."

"Ma! Ma!" Elizabeth danced up and down at the door, her long skirts swishing around her ankles. "Here comes Pa!"

Sure enough, Pa's wagon was rolling into the barn lot. George shouted, "Pa's home!"

Little Herman started chanting, "Pa's home! Pa's home!"

Mother stood up from her work. She smoothed her apron down and brushed back the tendrils of hair from her face. Her cheeks were pink from the work of pounding the cabbage.

George and his brothers gathered round their father as he came up the walk. "Did you get the metal you need?" John asked.

"Yes, son, enough for a while, I think."

Mother opened the door. "You look tired."

"I am, Emmeline," Pa said, smiling wearily. "It's a tiresome trip to drive a wagon all the way to Schenectady for these metal parts for the threshing machines. We can make all the wooden parts here in our own shop, but we have to get the metal in Schenectady."

"Isn't there any other place to get the metal?" asked Jay.

"Yes, son, but Schenectady is the closest." Father looked at the kraut-making all around him. "What do I see here? All the kraut is being made without my help?"

"It sure is, Pa, and we're almost done." George looked at his mother. "Aren't we, Ma? The barrel is getting full."

"That's right. Just a little more to do." Mother turned to Father to ask, "When will you have to go back to Schenectady again?"

"I may not have to, Emmeline. Mr. Clute of the foundry in Schenectady has some ideas on how we could get our metal more easily. He is coming down to talk to us soon."

50

It was soon winter time, and there were many suppers of pork and sauerkraut. The long gray days were spent in school. Jacob and George usually walked to school together. Then they ran home after school to romp in the snow, slide on the hills, or just wrestle with each other.

After supper was cleared away, George and his brothers sat around the kitchen table to do their homework. The coal oil lamp in the center of the table cast its flickering mellow light over their books. Its light threw strange shadows in the corners of the kitchen. George sat with his chin on his hands and watched the flickering flame and the black smoke wisp trailing up from it. The pungent odor of the burning coal oil smelled good. George felt comfortable and happy.

Then he turned to look at Herman toddling from his mother to his father. Instead of looking at his books George held out his hands to Herman. The little boy ran unsteadily to his brother.

George thought Herman was especially cute with his big eyes and fair hair. He liked to play with his little brother. It was much more fun than doing homework.

"Herman, come now!" Mother laid her mending aside and stretched her arms to her youngest son. "It's time for you to go to bed." Then she turned to George. "Son, it is time for you to do your homework. Don't put it off any longer."

George sighed and looked back at his books. He wasn't thinking about the words on the page though. His blue eyes looked far away as he thought about spring, and then the summer days when school would be out. No more homework!

It was only a few months until his dreams came true. Again he and Jacob could spend their days running in the fields, and he could work on his machines. He whittled and worked until his wooden machines would work. He already had many new ideas he wanted to try.

One afternoon in June, as he came walking down the road, he saw a strange horse and buggy tied in front of his house.

George looked at the strange buggy. He was sure he had never seen it before. Quietly he slipped in the kitchen door. He could hear voices in the parlor. He wondered who was there.

A man's voice said clearly, "Mr. Westinghouse, I think you would be very wise to consider moving your business to Schenectady."

Another man's voice continued, "We have found a fine location for the shop on the Erie Canal near the railroad. It is right by the foundries and machine shops where you can get the metal you need. Schenectady is a center of transportation. It will be easy for you to get the necessary materials to build your machinery. It will also be easy to send your finished machinery to your customers. You'll save time and money."

George frowned. The crease between his eyebrows deepened as he tried to puzzle out what they meant. Then he heard his father's answer.

"Mrs. Westinghouse and I have talked about this move. We have agreed that it will be best to move our family and our business to Schenectady. It is time to make the change."

George's chest felt tight. Pa must mean that the family would leave Central Bridge and move to Schenectady! He sat down. His eyes felt hot and dry. He didn't know whether he would like to live in another town! The family would leave this house and the valley. He wondered if the others knew. Then he thought of his friend Jacob. He would be moving away from Jacob too! He'd have to go tell Jacob.

George ran out the door and down the road. He ran all the way to Jacob's house. He couldn't even think how it would be to live anywhere else but Central Bridge.

54

"Jacob! Jacob!" George called as he swung open the front gate.

Jacob came to the kitchen door. "I can't play now. I've got to do my chores."

George was breathing fast. "I know, but I have to talk to you." He took a deep breath. "Jacob, we're going to move!"

"What do you mean?" Jacob looked puzzled. "Who is going to move?"

"Pa and all of us! Some men are in our parlor right now talking to Ma and Pa. Pa is going to move the shop to Schenectady!"

"Schenectady!" Jacob's eyes were wide. He just couldn't believe it! "Are you sure?"

"I guess I'm sure." George sat down on a stump. "Doesn't seem like it could be real." He looked at his friend. "Jacob, you know we might not ever see each other again."

Jacob sat down beside him. "Schenectady is a long ways away. I reckon we might not."

As unreal as such a change seemed to George, the Westinghouse family actually was going to move. There was a short, very busy time until all the belongings were packed. Then the Westinghouse family started on the journey.

George rode in the wagon with his older brothers. John and Jay sat up on the seat and drove the horses. George and Albert sat on the back and swung their legs. They didn't seem to mind leaving the old neighborhood.

Jacob was standing under the big tree by the road. His eyes were round and blue and very shiny as he watched the boys drive away. His hands were jammed deep in his pockets.

George waved and waved to his friend until he could see only a blur standing where Jacob should be. He looked again at the white house behind the big lacy locust trees. Then he rubbed his eyes and nose on his sleeve with a swipe of his arm.

It was a long journey to Schenectady. The new house was pleasant, but it didn't feel like home. After a few days though, with Ma in the kitchen at the hot cookstove, with the familiar smells of food wafting through the room, the big table in the center of the room, and the heavy cupboard in the corner, George began to feel as though he belonged in this house.

Father's new shop was exciting too. It was in a big stone building down by the Erie Canal. George became greatly interested in the strange new sounds and sights of the busy city, the canal with the heavily laden barges gliding by, the trains puffing into town, and the great old bridge draping across the Mohawk River.

The heat of the August sun beat down on George's head as he sat on the canal bank near Father's shop. He was watching the horses, which were pulling a boat on the canal. He looked up to see a boy, just about his size walking up to him.

"Do you want to fight?" asked the boy calmly.

George stood up. The boy, who was about as tall as he, had dark hair and clear blue eyes. The boy didn't look angry.

"I guess not," George answered.

"Fraidy cat," retorted the boy.

"I am not!" George frowned. Why should a boy he didn't even know come and call him a fraidy cat? He stuck out his jaw and raised his fists. "If you want a fight, you got it!"

The challenger put up his fists, but he didn't move to hit George. His voice was friendly. "I'm Matt Schroder. Who are you?"

George boxed a little with his fists as he answered, "I'm George Westinghouse."

Matt pointed to the shop. "Does that place belong to your pa?"

"Yup," answered George.

George saw a man walking down the canal bank. The man was tall and straight, and he was walking softly and swiftly. He looked strange. He had long straight black hair. He wore no hat or shoes. He was carrying a basket on his arm.

"Who is he?" George almost whispered.

Matt turned to see what had taken George's attention. "Who? Oh, that's Jim Cuff, the Indian medicine man."

"Why is he coming here?" asked George.

"He goes all over town and sells his medicine to sick people," Matt said. "He can really make you well, too. One time I was sick and Ma got medicine from Jim. I got well right away!"

George couldn't stop looking at the strange figure. Jim Cuff's black hair hung down about his long, solemn face. His dark eyes seemed to look straight at George.

Matt laughed. "You don't need to be afraid of Jim Cuff!"

George turned to glare at Matt. "That's the second time you've called me afraid. And I don't even know you yet!" He put up his fists again and got ready to really swing. His face was red with anger. "I'm not afraid of anybody, and I'll show you right now!"

Matt backed up a little. "I believe you. I didn't really want to fight. I just wanted to make your acquaintance. Maybe we'll be friends."

George still glared at Matt, but he put his fists down slowly. "Maybe we will."

.

Useless Toys

GEORGE AND MATT did become friends. George made other friends too. The boys took George to see all the sights in Schenectady. They went swimming in the Mohawk River. They watched the trains belching smoke and sparks as they pulled in from Albany. They sat and watched the barges go up the Erie Canal. They saw the broomcorn factory where brooms were made, and they went past the locomotive factory. There were many things to see and do in Schenectady!

Soon, though, it was time for school again. Mr. Westinghouse hoped that George would do better in school in Schenectady than he had in Central Bridge. George did try, but he couldn't help looking forward to the things he could do after school was out for the day.

One warm autumn day George was waiting for the dismissal bell to ring. He slumped over his desk. The schoolroom was quiet except for the droning of the teacher's voice.

"Every sentence must have a verb, a word that tells what the subject is doing or being. For example, 'George runs.'"

George straightened in his seat. He thought she was calling on him!

But, after clearing her throat, Miss Dietz went on in her same quiet voice. "The verb 'runs' tells what George is doing . . ."

George looked at the clock. Its slow, regular ticking was bringing it almost to four o'clock, when they would be out of school again. With a loud click the minute hand made the final effort and landed straight up. The bell clapper started its task of bonging out the four strikes on the bell. How good it was to hear those four strikes! Miss Dietz waited until the striking was finished and then said wearily, "Class dismissed."

The room was filled with the scraping of chairs and the shuffling of feet as the pupils filed out, pushing one another.

"George! George!" Matt called.

"What about going down to the canal to watch the barges?" Matt asked, hurrying up to George.

That sounded like a dandy idea. It was always fun to watch the barges. George hesitated a moment. "I want to go down to the shop first. I'll tell you what! I'll meet you back by the canal in an hour or so."

"Fine," Matt said. "I have to go home to do some chores for Ma. I'll see you then."

George ran straight to the shop. He put his books down in a corner and went to an empty workbench. He felt good because he was out of school for the rest of the day. Now he could work on the machine that he was building.

Father came up beside him just as he was getting his work laid out before him. "Hello, son. I'm glad you're here. I want you to watch Mr. Campbell make the plate for the new threshing machine. Then you'll know how it's done."

George looked at his work. He could just see how the parts could be put together. He had wanted to finish his water wheel this afternoon before he went to meet Matt. George sighed to himself and followed his father.

"Stephen, I want George to see how you are making this plate," Father instructed.

Stephen Campbell smiled at George. "All right, boy, stand there and you can see all I do. Ask questions if you don't understand."

George stood at the foreman's elbow. "Didn't you used to work for Pa in Central Bridge before you went to Chicago?"

"I did, and then I went out to Chicago in 1852. I stayed there until just this year, when your Pa asked me to come here to be a foreman in his new shop," explained Mr. Campbell.

"I'm glad you did come back here to work," George said. He liked Stephen Campbell.

The foreman smiled. "I am too, but right now you and I had better get to work!"

He went on with his work. George stood first on one foot and then on the other as he watched. Mr. Campbell used one tool and then another. He turned and twisted his work. He fastened it into a clamp, he bent and sawed a little, and he drilled a hole. Then he carefully filed the corners so that it would be nice and smooth.

George clasped his hands behind his back. Then he unclasped them and folded his arms across his chest. He lowered his head a bit to look out the window to see if he could see Matt out by the canal. He could see the gay fall colors

65

of the trees blending into one another. The scarlet reds of the oaks, the orange golds of the maples, and the brilliant yellows all flowed together into a beautiful sea of color. He could feel the crisp, yet warm air coming in the open window.

Mr. Campbell looked at the boy standing there and saw the faraway look in his blue eyes. George was staring out the window. The foreman chuckled to himself. The work was going much too slowly to hold George's interest. The boy was tired of watching the painstaking work.

Mr. Campbell rubbed the top of George's head with his hand. "George, how would you like to watch your brother John for a while as he works on metal for the thresher?"

"Oh yes, sir," George answered.

"Mr. Westinghouse!" George's father turned in answer to the call.

"Mr. Westinghouse, I think George has seen all there is to be seen about this work."

"Very well, George. You go to John's bench now. See how much you can learn."

George ran across the room to stand by John at his work.

A QUARREL

Mr. Westinghouse stood straight and tall as he watched his young son run across the room. His eyes were warm and kind. George was a good boy, but he must be taught a trade. He should learn to use tools by watching others use them properly. Suddenly a frown deepened above his eyes as he heard the voices of his sons grow loud. Why did the boys quarrel so often?

George's voice was high and shrill as he shouted above the noise of the shop, "You could do that much more easily if—"

John, his big brother, shouted back, "I suppose you could do it better!"

"Yes I could! Just let me—"

Father strode over to John's workbench with firm, heavy steps. "What is wrong, boys?"

John scowled as he turned to his father. "George won't keep still and watch. He keeps telling me how to do my work!"

"It would take just half the time," George replied angrily, "if he would only use—"

"George! That's enough!" Mr. Westinghouse interrupted. He felt greatly annoyed. If only George would just stand and learn!

"Father, let me go to that bench," George demanded. "I'll show him how to do it!"

"George!" Father stood and looked at both his sons. "All right, George, you may go to the bench and work, but you don't need to do your brother's work. He can do well enough himself."

Mr. Campbell watched George go to a bench and bend down to his own work. Then he looked at Mr. Westinghouse's grim face. He knew how it concerned Mr. Westinghouse that George didn't seem to want to do things the way other people did. Then he glanced back at George hard at work on his own machine. He smiled. George would be all right.

George leaned over his own work. It made him feel good to be able to fit pieces together and have them do what he wanted them to do. He made wheels which would go round and turn other wheels. He made shafts go back and forth. He fastened little wheels to big pieces of wood and big wheels to little pieces of wood. He joined them together with pins. He made the entire machine move just the way he wanted it to.

His fair head bent over the bench, and his hands were busy with the work he was doing. He didn't know the time. George didn't even know how long he had been working, but he had just about finished his machine when he saw a shadow fall across his bench.

70

He looked up to see his father standing beside him. Father picked up George's machine. Two or three small pieces fell off.

"George, what are you making?"

"A machine, Pa," George answered.

"For what?" asked Mr. Westinghouse in a quiet but very stern voice.

George felt a little puzzled. His eyebrows drew down into a deep crease between his eyes. He sighed. Really he just wanted to see if he could make it work. He knew his father would never understand how he felt. He answered lamely, "I guess, for nothing, Pa."

"For nothing!" Father exclaimed. He picked up some of the other work from the back of the bench. "This you made yesterday. Is this for nothing too?" One by one Mr. Westinghouse picked up all the things which George had made and took them out to the trash heap. George watched his father with dismay.

"George, these things are nothing but trumpery! You should not be wasting your time on useless toys. You should be learning—learning at school and learning here at the shop." Pa sounded tired. "Now go on home. I'll talk to you later."

Mr. Westinghouse threw away all the work George had done. George wondered sadly where he could make his machines from now on. He still had so many things he wanted to make!

The Haunted Bridge

GEORGE FELT tired as he walked out of the shop. He plodded along through the dust of the yard as he walked slowly down toward the canal. He had lost everything that mattered to him.

"Hey, George! What happened?" asked Matt.

George looked up to see Matt running toward him from the canal bank. Matt was shouting, "Hey, George, you missed a huge barge of lumber going to Buffalo!"

"Father threw out all my work," George answered in a discouraged voice.

"What do you mean?" asked Matt. "You were supposed to meet me here a long time ago."

George had completely forgotten about meeting Matt. "Oh Matt, I'm sorry!" Then he explained, "I got to working on my machine, and it really worked just the way I expected it to!"

"Good! But come on now. Listen! I hear some singing. Another barge must be coming."

The two boys ran down to the bank. They looked at the mirror smoothness of the water. Through the grey dusk of evening a broad barge loomed. A mule, walking along the tow path, dragged the barge slowly through the water. The mule had its head lowered. Its long ears were laid back. The animal walked slowly as though it were working hard to pull the heavy load. The boys were sorry for the tired little animal.

"Hi!" the boys called to the driver.

The big husky man on the front of the barge smiled and waved back at Matt and George. He opened his mouth and started to sing. His low voice filled the quiet evening.

"I've got a mule, her name is Sal,
Fifteen miles on the Erie Canal.
She's a good ole worker, and a good old pal,
Fifteen miles on the Erie Canal.

We've hauled some barges in our day,
Filled with lumber, coal, and hay,
And we know every inch of the way
From Albany to Buffalo.

Low bridge! Everybody down!
Low bridge, for we're going through a town,
And you'll always know your neighbor,
You'll always know your pal,
If you've ever navigated on the Erie Canal."

The boys waved again as the barge floated past them. They watched the V shaped ripples which followed the barge. They could still hear the driver singing. The song sounded strange as it floated back from farther and farther away.

George and Matt stretched on the bank to listen. George still felt discouraged.

"Looking at the water makes me want to dive in and swim," said Matt.

George looked at the inviting, shining water. "Matt, you know we dare not go swimming in the canal! We've both promised we'd never even try it, and now it's almost winter."

"I reckon you're right," Matt agreed. "What about going down to the swimming hole in the Mohawk River? That's just as much fun."

"Oh Matt, it's really too chilly to swim." George didn't sound very interested.

"Well, come on, George." Matt pulled on his friend's arm. "Let's do something!"

George walked along slowly beside Matt, but he kept looking back at the shop.

"Aw George," Matt said, "come on, let's race."

George grinned at this suggestion. He could outrun Matt any day. "You bet!" he answered.

They ran and ran till they were both panting for breath and the sweat was running down George's forehead. He began to feel better. It was a wonderful evening. The large trees were so pretty. Their drooping limbs were covered with gaily colored leaves. Some of the oak leaves looked almost purple in the evening twilight. The golden leaves stood out as though they were candle flames. The disappointment of the shop began to feel far away.

THE ICE FLOES

In a few weeks the autumn leaves fell to the ground and the snow of winter came. George was sorry that he couldn't do his own work at the shop after school. Some afternoons he would go in and just stand around and watch the men at work. When his father saw him, he could usually find a task for George to do.

Most afternoons, though, he went with the boys. Sometimes they went sledding or skating, and sometimes they would have snowball fights. Wintertime was an exciting time!

The Mohawk River clogged with ice. Then, as the spring thaws came, the ice floes broke loose and came hurtling down the river.

One chilly day, as winter was beginning to fade and the first few signs of spring appeared, George and his friends were very excited.

"Let's all go down to the Mohawk Bridge after school," Richard said to the whole group of boys at recess time. "The ice is breaking up in the river and Pa says the bridge will go out!"

"Do you really think the bridge will fall?" asked Matt excitedly.

George was defiant. "The Mohawk bridge won't be knocked down by any old ice chunks!"

"Pa says it will!" Richard said scornfully

Will, who was watching George and Richard, said excitedly, "Let's go down and just see!"

The boys could hardly wait for school to be out. They rushed from the schoolyard and started running down the brick walks to Washington Street and up to the end of the bridge. A crowd had gathered to watch the dark bridge and the ice in the churning river.

Matt shook his head. "It is bound to fall!"

"Oh, no, Matt, it couldn't fall down!" exclaimed George. "See how it's suspended from strong, heavy planks of wood."

Richard laughed at George. "Look at those huge chunks of ice coming toward it. Wait until the bridge gets the pressure of all that ice on the piers which hold it up."

"Those piers don't hold it up, Richard! The bridge is suspended from those strong pieces of wood. It couldn't possibly fall!" He knew by the way the bridge was built that it was sound, but he didn't know how to tell the others.

Matt frowned as he looked at the huge old covered bridge. It seemed to hang in festoons. Each section was lower in its center than at the ends, and the long, long bridge was made up of

many of these drooping sections. Each one looked as though it were ready to fall, even without the blows of the crushing ice floes.

A raw biting wind whipped around the bridge. The wind blew into the openings of the bridge and the many cracks in its sides. The river below rolled and tossed the heavy chunks of ice.

"Look! Look! That will take it for sure!" shouted a man pointing to a huge pile of ice against one of the stone bases of the bridge.

Just then a churning of the river forced a mighty blast behind the piled-up ice. The bridge groaned, but the ice, not the bridge broke up! Crunching as it went, the ice flowed on down the river past the bridge.

"That was a close one! The next one will take her for sure!" shouted Richard.

George was so excited that he felt hot. He, too, had been afraid. It looked as if that ice was too much. Would the bridge fall?

"Let's go up and ask Uncle Stoeffel what he thinks," cried Matt. Mr. Christopher Beekman, the tollkeeper, was called Uncle Stoeffel by all the boys. No one could even remember how the nickname had started.

The boys went up to the shanty door. "Come in," called Uncle Stoeffel. The tollkeeper sat calmly in his chair. He was smoking his pipe and stroking his big old cat that helped him tend the bridge. The gray smoke from his pipe filled his small rooms.

"Evening, boys. Want to go across?"

"Cross!" exclaimed Richard. "I certainly don't! It's going to fall down!"

"It will take more than that ice to take this bridge down," said the old man.

GHOSTS IN THE BRIDGE

George and Matt looked with fascination at the dark insides of the bridge. There were two dull, smoking coal-oil lamps on either side of the two roadways which went through the bridge.

Feeling a little daring, they went up close to the entrance of the bridge and peeked in. The dark sides of the bridge, which enclosed the roadways, narrowed down until they could see just a faint patch of the evening twilight at the other end. The beams of the bridge threw ghostly shadows which made the boys shudder.

"Doesn't it look spooky?" whispered Matt.

The old timbers of the bridge creaked, and the wind whistled and moaned through the darkness. George's head went forward a bit as he tried hard to see without getting any closer. "Do you suppose there are any ghosts in there?"

"How many ghosts do you think haunt the bridge?" Uncle Stoeffel asked.

Richard didn't look as though he believed the tollkeeper, but the other three boys looked carefully at Mr. Beekman. George's blue eyes grew wide. He looked hard at Uncle Stoeffel's face to see whether he could be teasing.

"Are there really ghosts in there?" asked Matt earnestly.

Uncle Stoeffel drew deeply on his pipe. "Some say there are." He smiled at the boys.

Richard and Will ran down the road without waiting to hear any more. Matt and George started to back away, but they stared at the inside of the bridge as though their eyes were glued. They couldn't take their eyes from the inside. They were afraid they might see one of the ghosts. Yet they were afraid they might not.

"I expect it's about time for you two to be home at your supper tables," the old man reminded them kindly.

George looked quickly about him at the darkening world. "Oh Matt, I bet we're already late. We'd better hurry!"

But as they ran down the cobblestone street both boys turned their heads back for a final look at the 'haunty' bridge.

A Surprise
for George

George ran fast to get home. It seemed to be getting darker with every step he took. His footsteps sounded louder and louder in his ears as he ran along the brick sidewalk. Lights were gleaming from the windows in the houses.

As he came to his own front gate he could see the soft golden lamplight in the dining room. Soon he could smell the good food. The family had already gathered around the supper table.

He didn't look up as he slipped into his chair at the table as quickly and as quietly as he could. When he did raise his head he noticed that Albert's chair was still empty.

"Where have you been?" asked Mother.

"We all went down to watch the bridge," George answered. "The ice was breaking up, and everyone thought the bridge would go out!"

"It would be a great loss if it did. The bridge didn't go, did it son?" Pa asked with concern.

"No, Pa," George said. "That bridge is still good and strong."

"Many of the men were talking about the heavy thaws," Mr. Westinghouse explained to his wife. "They were afraid that the old bridge might collapse under the force of the ice floes coming down the river from upstream."

"My, that would be dreadful if the bridge went out!" Mother shook her head.

"It won't, Ma. You don't need to worry about that bridge now," George assured his mother. "You should have seen the way the ice pounded at it! And the bridge is just as solid as it ever was. You don't have to worry about it."

86

"Emmeline, that bridge was built by Theodore Burr a little over fifty years ago," Mr. Westinghouse explained to his wife. "He was one of the finest bridge architects in the country."

Mrs. Westinghouse nodded her head. "Was he related to Aaron Burr?"

"As a matter of fact he was. He and Aaron Burr were cousins." Father turned back to George. "Was your brother Albert with you?"

"No, Pa, he wasn't down at the bridge." George continued, "Uncle Stoeffel said you don't have to worry about the bridge going out." Then he hesitated. He didn't know whether he ought to go on or not. "He did say there are ghosts on the bridge, though."

"George!" exclaimed his mother. "Are you sure that's what he said?"

George thought a moment before he answered slowly. "I guess what he said was that some people say there are ghosts."

"That is a little more like it," Father said, smiling. "Chris was teasing you."

"Oh, George, you know there is no such thing as a ghost!" John laughed.

"Well, maybe not. But if there are any, I'm sure that's where they would want to stay!" retorted George.

A LIGHT AT THE SHOP

The front door swung open and closed. Everyone looked toward the front hall to see Albert walk in. He was very surprised to feel all the eyes upon him. He didn't realize that he was late. He hurried to the table.

Father looked very stern. "Son, it is time you learned to be prompt for meals."

"Where have you been?" asked Mother.

Albert quickly slid into his chair. "I am sorry, but I didn't think you were home yet, Pa. There was still a light on at the shop as I passed, so I didn't hurry."

"A light?" asked Father. "Where?"

"Up in the loft. I thought you were still working. I didn't think I was late."

"I wonder . . ." Father looked puzzled.

John asked, "Who could it be?"

"I don't know!" Father frowned. "It could have been Stephen Campbell, though I thought he was finished with his work and ready to leave when we did. I'd better find out."

The next day at school George and his friends were talking about the ghosts on the bridge. George added, "There is something peculiar at Pa's shop, too. Last night there was a light in the loft," he lowered his voice, "after everyone had gone home!"

"Why, two or three times this week I've seen a light in the loft at your pa's shop," said Will. "After quitting time, too, on my way home."

Matt leaned forward with great interest. "Do you think maybe there are ghosts there too?"

"Of course not!" Richard said scornfully. "You know there is no such thing as a ghost!"

"Then why did you run away from the bridge so fast last night?" George asked.

Richard glared at George, but before he could retort, Joe remarked, "My grandmother says there used to be lots of ghosts in the Mohawk Valley." Then Joe came a little closer and whispered, "Particularly Indian ghosts!"

"Uncle Stoeffel said there were ghosts on the bridge!" said Will. "If they can go there, they can go other places too!"

"Oh, you're all a bunch of babies!" sneered Richard. "Nobody believes that stuff any more."

Just then the school bell rang out that recess was over. The boys filed in quietly, but all of them were glaring at Richard. He thought he was so smart!

That afternoon, though, George found that there was a very good reason for the lights at night at the shop.

As usual after school George walked down to Pa's shop. He trudged along slowly, though. It wasn't much fun to go down there now. He never knew what he could do when he got there.

His father had thrown out all his work. He had no place to make anything else. He wanted to be working with his own hands, but he would probably have to stand and watch John.

George swung open the door and went in. The inside of the shop looked dark and gloomy after the bright sunshine outside. He jammed his hands down into his pockets and very slowly walked over to John's bench. On the way he kicked a piece of scrap metal aside.

Suddenly there was someone standing squarely in front of him. He lifted his head slowly. He

91

knew it would be Pa telling what he could do today, and it wouldn't be anything interesting.

"George."

He looked up to see Stephen Campbell instead of his father standing there.

"Come with me," the foreman told him curtly.

"Yes sir." George was surprised.

Stephen Campbell walked through the shop, past his own bench and past John's bench. He kept walking past the big farm machinery. George wondered where Mr. Campbell was taking him. Mr. Campbell had sounded stern. Could something be wrong?

As they reached the very back of the shop the foreman started up the stairs to the loft. George stopped at the bottom of the stairs.

"Come on, George," said Stephen Campbell as he motioned George to follow him.

When they reached the loft, Mr. Campbell stepped aside. "This is for you," he told George.

George stared straight ahead. He couldn't believe his eyes! He didn't understand!

The foreman smiled. "This is a bench with
tools where you can work."

George looked at the workbench with all the
tools laid out neatly. A stool stood in front of it.
"You mean it's for me!" he exclaimed.

Stephen Campbell was pleased with the boy's happiness. "A place of your own, George, to work on whatever you wish."

George's blue eyes grew wide as he realized that it was Stephen Campbell who had the light in the loft. "It was you here last night working!" he exclaimed. "It wasn't a ghost!"

"After my own work was done, George, it took only a few evenings' work."

George grinned. "Then you were the ghost!"

"I don't think so!" The foreman laughed. "Did you think I was a ghost?"

"Oh, we saw the lights, and—" Suddenly George thought of something else. "Does Pa know?" His blue eyes grew dark, and his face was serious. What if his father objected!

"No, your father doesn't know," Mr. Campbell replied slowly, "but I'm sure—"

"George! Are you up there?" Father's voice came up the stairway, loud and clear.

George's answer was little and weak. "Yes, sir." The palms of his hands felt moist and cold as he held them tightly together. His father's footsteps came nearer, and soon Mr. Westinghouse stood at the top of the stairs.

Father's face looked stern, but his eyes were kind as he looked at the little workshop in the loft. "You did this, Stephen?" he asked.

"Yes, sir. After hours. I brought a few of my own things up." Stephen Campbell sounded kind and sure. "I thought George could work up here out of the way of the work downstairs. He needs a place to do his own work."

Anxiously George watched his father's face. He felt relief and a good warmness within him as he saw his father smile slowly.

Mr. Westinghouse looked straight into George's face and said, "All right, son, sit down at your bench then, and go to work."

A Bargain

GEORGE DID get down to work. As soon as school hours were over he would hurry to the shop to go to work on his own machines. The little shop in the loft became more and more crowded as George finished work and shoved it into a corner. Then he would start something else.

He would work and work, with his head bent over and his mouth tight, until his job would come out just right. He would whittle and trim, and he would fit. Belts would go on just right or be taken off and pieces moved until the parts fitted. One afternoon in the spring of 1860, Mr. Westinghouse came up to the loft.

He shook his head. The little loft was cluttered with all the things George had made. George's father felt it was time for his son to work on more useful products.

"George," Father called. He thought it was good that George enjoyed his work so much. Surely he must be learning something about tools and workmanship. George was so busy at his work that he didn't hear his father's voice.

Mr. Westinghouse spoke a little louder. "George, I would like to speak to you."

The boy jumped off his stool. "Yes, sir. I am sorry. I didn't hear you come up."

"I know you were working, son," Father said, "but I want to talk to you."

George swallowed hard and put his hand up to his mouth. What could Pa want? He tried to think of anything wrong he had done.

Father could tell that George was wondering what was to be said. "Son, I am glad you have the opportunity to work here. I am sure your are enjoying yourself. I am also sure you must be learning something about mechanics. Now, though, you are nearly fourteen years old, and I think it is time you go to work in the shop to help build the farm machinery which we sell."

George was troubled. "Pa, I don't have to give up my bench, do I?"

"No, George, that was not what I meant. You may work at your own bench in your free time and make whatever you choose. However, you ought to spend most of your after-school time working in the shop and making useful things."

George felt better. So long as he didn't have to give up his own work, he would like to have a job in the shop. He could earn money to buy material for his own work.

"How much will I be paid?" George asked.

"Paid?" Mr. Westinghouse raised his eyebrows. "Do you think you should be paid?"

George thought for just a moment. His blue eyes were very serious, and a deep crease came between his eyebrows.

"Yes sir, I do," he answered his father. "All the men in the shop are paid for their work. If I work for you, surely my work must be worth something to you."

Mr. Westinghouse smiled a little to himself, but he took care that George didn't see it. He was pleased that his son was showing thoughts of being thrifty and earning something for his work. He cleared his throat and straightened his mouth into a serious line.

"Well, George, I'm willing to give you a chance at working. I will pay you fifty cents a day for every full day you work. On Saturdays when there is no school you may work all day. On other days you may count your hours until you have a whole day. As you see, you will be paid for the time you work for me."

George nodded his head. This seemed like a fair arrangement. He was already thinking of the materials he could buy with his money.

"Are you satisfied with this offer?" asked his father. "Will you go to work?"

"Yes sir, I will try it."

George did very well on his new job at the shop. He liked to make things, and he made them well. Mr. Campbell gave him the material and told him what was to done. It gave George pleasure to finish his part of the work.

One day Father stopped by George's bench and picked up the part which was almost finished. He turned the piece over in his hands and looked at it carefully. "This is done well, son," he said. It made George feel good to know his father was pleased with the work.

It was exciting, too, to see a new thresher roll out of the shop and to know that part of it was made by his own hands.

100

One Saturday morning in the summer of 1860, George Westinghouse was sitting at his work bench in his father's shop. He was hard at work on a part of the threshing machine. Then he heard a call, "Hey, George!"

He turned from his work to see who had called, and he saw Matt standing in the doorway. He answered, "Hi," and walked over to Matt. The warm sunshine was pouring through the door.

"Hi, George!" called Will from behind Matt. Joe and Richard were there too. "We're all going on a hike. Want to come along? asked Joe.

It was a beautiful summer day, just the kind which seems to pull a fellow outdoors. George liked to work and build machines, but he liked to swim and hike with his friends too.

He looked back at the dark, dusty shop. Then he looked out at the beautiful soft green world. The sky was pale blue with soft white clouds gliding through it. He took a deep breath. He certainly would like to go!

"Where are you going?" George asked.

"Oh, we don't know exactly," Matt answered. "Down by the bridge . . . maybe go swimming."

The sunshine came in the door all around Matt. George's face was covered with a wide grin. He could just think how much fun it would be. Then suddenly he stopped smiling. All at once he thought about his job. He caught his lip between his teeth as he thought.

"What's wrong?" asked Matt.

"I'll have to ask Pa," George answered slowly. He didn't really want to ask his father either, for he was sure what the answer would be.

"Why?" asked Matt. "Can't we just go? He won't need to know about it."

George shook his head. "No, I'm supposed to work on Saturday. That was the bargain I made. I'll have to ask Pa."

"Well, all right," Matt said. "We'll see you down by the bridge."

George stood watching his friends as they ran down the cobblestone street. Suddenly his father called, "George, come over here!"

Pa was standing by a large pile of pipe. "I'm going to go out of town on business for a few days. While I am gone I would like you to cut this pipe into pieces each two feet long." Mr. Westinghouse continued to explain, "This is hard work, and I expect it will take all your spare time for the next few days. I hope you will have the job nearly finished by the time I return."

George was standing with his mouth half opened the entire time his father was speaking. He was trying to find the right time to speak.

"Father, I was just going to ask you if I could go on a hike with the boys. They're going swimming, too. All the other boys are going."

"When?" Father asked, frowning.

George spoke quickly. "Today, Pa." He went on before his father could say anything. "We're going to have lots of fun."

Father's mouth looked firm and tight. "George, did you not ask that I pay you to work here?"

George's forehead wrinkled. "Well, yes sir." He hesitated. "But Pa, I'll do the work afterwards! Please let me take today off!"

Father's face did not change. "George, a good citizen does not back out of a bargain the first time some fun comes along. You made a bargain, and I expect you to live up to your word." He turned and pointed to the huge stack of uncut pipe. "I was counting on you to do this job, and I think you ought to do it!"

As his father turned and left, George stood looking at the pipe. He was thinking fast. Then he started to smile. He could just see in his thoughts what he needed to do to cut the pipe just the way his father wanted it!

Quickly he went to work. He got some tools, arranged them carefully, and attached them to a power machine.

He placed his contraption by the pile of pipe. Then he stacked the pipe so it would feed into the machine. He adjusted some screws and levers. When he started the machine running, a wide grin spread over his face. He watched carefully as each piece of pipe fed into the machine, came out perfectly cut, and dropped into a neat pile.

George snapped his fingers and exclaimed to himself with glee. "This will do it!"

For the first time since he had begun he looked out the window. It must be nearly noon, but if he hurried he could catch up with the boys. The clicking of the pipe as it went through the machine made a nice sound.

"This will work fine," he thought. "But what if something jams and it stops working!" He scratched his head for a moment.

Then he looked over at the foreman, Stephen Campbell. George had the answer!

"Mr. Campbell! Mr. Campbell! Would you mind watching my pipe cutting while I'm gone?"

"Didn't your father say you were to stay here and work today?" the foreman asked sternly.

"No," George answered thoughtfully, "he didn't. He told me I was to cut this pipe, and I will! It doesn't matter that it is being cut while I'm away." George set his mouth and said with determination, "When I grow up and have men working in my shop, I'm going to give all of them Saturday afternoon off!"

Mr. Campbell was surprised when he saw George's machine for cutting the pipe. "All right," he agreed, "I'll watch it."

"Oh thanks, Mr. Campbell." George gave the foreman a few instructions.

Then he scrambled out of his work apron and ran out to find his friends.

The Ghost on
the Bridge

THE SUNSHINE was warm on George's head as he
ran down the cobblestone streets. He felt so
good. He had done the job his father had asked
him to do, and he was still going to be able to
have fun with his friends. He knew exactly where
to find them. They would be at the swimming
hole in the Mohawk River.

He could hardly wait to get there. He became
hotter by the minute. The cool water would
feel so good! He ran across the fields and among
the trees. The water sparkled in the sunshine.
Then he saw the boys and heard their happy
voices as they played in the water.

"Hey, there's George!" called Matt. Will and Joe waved, and Richard yelled, "Come on in!"

George took off his clothes as fast as he could, dropping them as he ran toward the water. "Oh!" he shivered with delight as he went into the cold water. With a splash he plopped into the pool. He swam over to Matt.

"Watch me!" cried Matt. He clambered out on the bank and grabbed a nearby tree branch. He crawled out on the branch and, swinging from it like a monkey, dropped into the water below. What fun it was!

George took a deep breath and dived under the water. The cool smooth water closed in about him. He slid through the water, feeling like a slim, swift fish.

"Here, catch it!" Will shouted as he threw a ball at George. George leaped far out of the water, but the ball just touched the top of his fingers and bounced into the water behind him.

Matt swam after it and, as George tried to reach for it, they both fell into the water with a mighty splash! When they stood up, rubbing the water from their eyes, they could see that Will had the ball again!

They romped and splashed and played. They dived from an old tree trunk which extended out into the water. It was all wonderful fun.

Matt, tired out from swimming and diving, went to the bank and started to rub himself dry with his shirt. He looked down where he could see the old dark bridge across the river. "Say, I have an idea! Let's explore the bridge!"

George was floating on his back and squinting his eyes into the bright sunlight. He saw beautiful patterns in the sky as he looked through the droplets of water on his dark eyelashes. He felt as though he could float here always.

"Say, that would be fun!" agreed Will. "Do you suppose there really are ghosts there?"

"There aren't any ghosts!" scoffed Richard as he joined the other boys on the bank. "Come on out, George. Lets show these ninnies that there aren't any ghosts!"

George opened his eyes and flipped over. He did know there weren't any ghosts. "All right, Richard, let's go!" He looked at the bridge. It did look very dark and fearful, though.

THE SHADOW

The boys quickly put on their clothes which had been strewn all over the bank. The clothes were damp and clammy over their wet bodies. Their hair was plastered down with water.

Uncle Stoeffel sat on his chair at the entrance of the bridge, with the smoke from his pipe floating off with the gentle breeze. His face crinkled into a merry smile as he watched the boys walking down the road together to the bridge. It was plain to him what they had been doing when he saw their wet heads and damp clothes. He also knew what they were going to do. For years boys had come to explore the haunted bridge. They were all anxious to find a ghost, yet scared to death that they might.

George, Richard, and Will entered the bridge ahead of Matt and Joe. The bridge had a funny smell. It smelled of old wood and the dampness and darkness of a shut-up old house. Little streams of sunlight fell down through the cracks in the roof.

"Step aside!" shouted Matt. "Hurry up! Here comes a carriage!"

The boys stepped off the firm roadway onto the big timbers at the side. They could hear the clippity-clopping of the horses that came trotting through, drawing a carriage. The horses went as fast as they dared. They didn't like going through the dark tunnel either.

112

Just after those wheels rolled by, a wagon, drawn by a heavy, tired plow horse, came from the other direction. Even that heavy, weary horse was trotting along as fast as he could. The farmer waved and called, "Hi, boys!" His voice rang through the hollow bridge.

Even such a cheery voice made them feel a little creepy. As they came close to the middle of the bridge, it was very dark. George drew his shoulders up a little. He felt a little chilly. He looked about at the high dark rafters, and the long grey shadows everywhere. He shivered a little. He wasn't exactly cold, but then he wasn't very warm any more either!

"What about those ghosts?" whispered Will.

"Oh, Will!" Richard was impatient. "You know as well as I do about ghosts!"

George looked down under his feet. Through the cracks in the floor he could see the water of the Mohawk River far below.

As the boards creaked and groaned, a high eerie sound, seemingly from nowhere, floated to them, "Boys! . . . Boys! . . ."

Will grabbed George's arm. George jumped. He just couldn't help it. Joe and Matt ran up, and they all huddled together. The sound still echoed through the rafters.

Cautiously George looked around. Richard was backing quietly toward the opening. George could see nothing . . . nothing but shadows. Who could tell what was in the shadows?

Suddenly a shadow started to move toward them. It came on swiftly and silently.

"Look!" cried Will.

Richard shrieked and wheeled to run out of the bridge. George looked up to see the shadow of a straight, ghostly figure.

A Surprise
for Father

THE BOYS didn't stop running until they were way down Washington Street. Richard was breathing in short, hard breaths, and his face looked as pale as a freshly-peeled potato! Joe didn't stop running until he caught up with Richard and the other boys. George looked back over his shoulder, but the entrance of the bridge held its secret in its blackness.

"What did you see?" George asked Richard.

"A tall, shadowy thing with long hair. It looked as if it was floating!" Richard answered breathlessly. "Its eyes looked right through me! It was coming toward me!"

"Did you see it?" Will asked Joe.

"I didn't see anything! I just saw the rest of you running, so I ran too!"

"I saw it and I heard it!" exclaimed Matt.

"Do you suppose it really was a ghost?" George asked slowly. He frowned. "Maybe—"

"Maybe what?" asked Matt.

"I don't know . . . just maybe . . ." George trailed off. He didn't really think there were ghosts. That is, he didn't think he did!

The boys started walking down the road.

"Now we know there really are ghosts," said Will. "We saw one!"

"Yes, we did," agreed Richard. "We did see one!" He still looked frightened as he asked slowly, "What do you suppose it wanted?"

" I don't think ghosts want anything, do they?" Matt replied. "Except maybe to scare folks."

"Oh my! Is that my father?" George asked as he saw a horse and buggy down the street.

116

"I thought you said your pa was going to be gone for several days," said Matt.

"I thought he was," answered George. "He said he was going away on business and wouldn't be back till next week."

"Well then, that must be someone else's buggy. It looks just like your pa's."

FATHER'S RETURN

Mr. Westinghouse smiled a little to himself as he drove down the cobblestone street in his buggy. He tugged the reins gently to make his horse go a bit faster. Molly's sharp hoofs clacked merrily as she broke into a trot.

Mr. Westinghouse was glad that he had finished his business early. It was a beautiful sunshiny day, the kind of day boys ought to be outside. He decided that he would let George go play with his friends. He was looking forward to getting back to the shop to tell George he could go out for a day's fun. It was still early. There would be plenty of time for the boy to have a good outing. Father smiled. He could just imagine how happy George would be.

The shop was dark and still when Mr. Westinghouse walked in. A few of the men were working in the back, but he didn't see George.

"George!" Father called when he didn't see his son at the usual workbench. "George!" he called again. His face grew serious and he frowned. He didn't hear pipe being cut nor the clanking sound as a piece of cut pipe falls to the floor.

Stephen Campbell looked up from his work when he heard Mr. Westinghouse call for George. The foreman laid his work on the bench and walked over to George's father. "Oh, Mr. Westinghouse, we didn't expect you so soon."

"Where is George?" Mr. Westinghouse asked. The line deepened between his dark eyebrows.

118

"Well, sir, he got—"

"Is George here?"

Campbell rubbed his chin. "Well, no sir, he isn't exactly here, but—"

"Then where exactly is he?" George's father interrupted. "He left against my instructions!" Mr. Westinghouse did not raise his voice, but it was plain to see that he was angry.

He had come back feeling very lenient toward George. He wanted his son to have a good time. But George had not kept his bargain!

Stephen Campbell was sorry that George's father was so upset. He wanted to tell the angry man about George's work, but Mr. Westinghouse had not given his foreman a chance to say anything or to show what George had done.

"Sir, please come with me." Stephen Campbell pointed to the stack of pipe in the corner of the shop. The whole stack was cut just the size it should be, and neatly piled.

George's father looked puzzled. His eyebrows drew down as he looked at the stack of pipe. Then he looked around to where the uncut stack had been when he had left that morning. There was no uncut stack! There was only the neat pile of pipe in two foot lengths!

"Is this the pipe I told George to cut?" asked Mr. Westinghouse in amazement.

"Yes sir," answered the foreman, "That is the pipe. And it is all cut just the way you said it should be."

Mr. Westinghouse rubbed his forehead with a handkerchief. He still couldn't believe or understand this. It would take days for one man to cut that much pipe.

"Who cut it?" he asked Campbell.

"George did it before he left," Campbell was glad to answer. "That is what I was trying to tell you when you asked where he was. He is with his friends, but he did his work first."

Stephen Campbell was relieved. He was glad to have Mr. Westinghouse know the whole story.

George's father looked around for a stool. He pulled one over and sat down heavily.

"What do you mean?" he asked. "How could he possibly have done this before he left? It would take a man at least three days to have cut all that pipe!"

Stephen Campbell smiled. Then he showed his employer the tools George had attached to the sawing machine to make the machine cut the pipe automatically.

"Well! Do tell! How on earth did that boy think of this!" Mr. Westinghouse shook his head in astonishment. He just stood and looked at the contraptions. Then he bent over and examined the way George had put the machine together.

"Do you mean to tell me that all that pipe went through here and was cut into the proper lengths?" he asked.

"That's right," said Campbell proudly, "and in a small part of the time it would take a man to do the same work by hand. There isn't a man in this shop who would have thought of it."

"Mr. Campbell! Mr. Campbell!" George's frightened voice interrupted the conversation.

Father looked up to see his son.

George ran into the shop calling, "Mr. Campbell, is the pipe all cut?" George had to know. Then he saw the two men standing together. His heart started to beat a little faster as he recognized his father. Pa wasn't supposed to be back until next week!

"Father," he cried, "I didn't think you would be back today!"

"I'm sure you didn't," his father said.

George felt a little ashamed because he had left when he was not supposed to. As he walked over to his father, he looked out of the corner of his eye to see if the pipe was all cut. What

122

a good sight to see it all neatly stacked just the way it ought to be! He lifted his eyes slowly to look at his father.

Mr. Westinghouse was looking squarely into George's eyes. His face had no expression. George didn't know what to expect, but he was certainly glad the work was finished.

Father stood looking at his son without saying anything. He was proud of the way George had fixed up the machine to make it work automatically, but he felt disappointed that George had left work against his wishes.

George wanted his father to say something, even to scold him! Mr. Westinghouse had often scolded George for suggesting faster methods of getting the work done.

Then Father said quietly, "Well, George, you did do what I asked you to do. You got the pipe all cut." He was silent a moment. Then he added, "And you did a very good job, too."

124

The Last of the Mohawks

AFTER SUPPER that night Mr. Westinghouse sat down heavily in his chair. His dark eyebrows were drawn together as he absentmindedly picked up the newspaper. He opened the pages in front of him, but he didn't read. He just looked off in a thoughtful stare.

Mrs. Westinghouse looked carefully at her husband. She wondered what was troubling him. He and her son George had both been very quiet during supper. She sat down in her chair across the room from her husband. She picked up some mending to do, as she rested after supper.

"Are you tired?" Mother asked quietly.

"No, Emmeline." Mr. Westinghouse laid his paper down on his lap. "It's not that I'm tired. I am both proud and perplexed. When I returned to the shop today, I found that George had rigged up a machine to cut pipe. His machine cut as much pipe in one day as it would take a man several days to cut."

Mrs. Westinghouse went on with her sewing without missing a stitch, but she smiled and her eyes twinkled. She knew how clever George was. From his behavior at supper she had felt he was up to something.

"He's very much like you, Father," she said.

Father's eyebrows did raise, and his eyes looked dark with surprise. "Like me! Oh?"

"When George sees a need for something he does it," she explained. "That is what I mean." She looked at her husband with pride.

"Do you remember the day George was born? You were busy working out a new part on a

126

threshing machine. When you came home you found your new son! I knew his name should be George, just like yours. He is good at working out ways to do things, just like you!"

A little quirk turned up the corners of Father's mouth. He remembered that day very well. He sighed though, as he continued, "There is more to this story, Emmeline. George rigged up this machine to cut the pipe so he would be able to go swimming with his friends!"

Mother rocked back and forth in her rocking chair as she stitched. "Well, George, he got the work done. It is natural for boys to like to romp and play. The other boys have all liked their fun, too."

Without lifting her head from her work, Mother glanced at Father.

"Maybe he should have more time for himself," she suggested.

"Perhaps you are right," he agreed.

Mr. Westinghouse was quiet for a long time. He rubbed his hand over his face. Then he rested his chin on his hand.

"Maybe what George needs is time to do things on his own," he said thoughtfully. "He certainly is clever in working things out."

Mrs. Westinghouse smiled as she went on with her sewing.

MAKING A VIOLIN

The boys were still excited about the ghost at the bridge. Now it was Richard who was sure there was a ghost.

The other boys who hadn't been with George and his friends would gather around to ask about their experience. "Was there really a ghost? Did you really see it?"

"I saw him with my own eyes," Richard declared, nodding his head wisely.

"It was very, very thin," he continued, lowering his voice. "You could almost see through it. It was tall, too."

"How tall?" they asked.

"Oh, about seven feet tall," Richard said.

George shivered. It had been a very frightening experience. None of the boys had been down to explore the bridge since!

All the boys who hadn't been with George and his friends wished they had. Gradually they did start to talk of other things, and it was several weeks before any of them saw their ghost again.

As George became interested in his work at the shop he seldom thought about the ghost. Pa gave him more time to work on his own things. Will Ratcliffe got a job at the shop, too, and worked at the bench next to George. After hours the two boys would work in the loft and make many different, wonderful things.

George even made a violin!

"Why should we make a violin?" Will asked George in surprise. He couldn't understand why George would want to make a violin.

"I read in a book at school about how a violin is made," George answered, "and I think we could make one. Then I could learn to play it."

So George did make a violin. Whenever he decided to do something, he set about to do it. After George and Will had worked on it for a long time, the instrument looked like a real violin! George smiled with pride as he smoothed and rubbed its wood finish. He turned the violin around to admire it.

"Will, I think I'll get someone to teach me to play it," he said.

George found a teacher to give him violin lessons. He practiced and practiced. He tried to follow all the directions the teacher gave him. But the noises which came from his violin were very sour!

130

Then one evening when they least expected it, the boys saw their ghost again! It started out as an ordinary summer evening. George was standing against the fence in front of his house, fiddling on his violin, when Matt and Richard came by. Each time he drew his bow across the strings it seemed the sound was worse.

"Why don't you give up?" called Matt.

Richard put his hands over his ears, and Matt exclaimed, "George, you can build them better than you can play them!"

George shook his head as he lowered the violin. Even he didn't like his own music.

His little brother Herman came running up. "Can I hold your violin, George?"

George handed the instrument to him. Herman tried to place it under his chin, but it just wouldn't fit! Matt and Richard laughed at Herman, and so did George.

131

"Where are you going?" George asked.

"Down by the circus grounds," Matt answered excitedly. "Want to come along? They're loading up the circus to leave town. All the wagons and everything will be going across the bridge."

"Sure, I'll come." George's face was pink with thinking about the fun of watching all the excitement. "Herman, take my violin inside and tell Ma where I'm going, will you?"

"Oh, George!" Herman looked at his brother hopefully. "Can I go too?"

The big boys looked at each other. "Sure, you can go. Just ask Ma," George answered.

"Wait for me! Please wait for me!" Herman cried as the boys started slowly down the walk. He kept looking back at them.

"We'll wait," George told him. "We'll just walk along slowly. Go on and ask."

"Ma! Ma!" Herman cried breathlessly as he ran into the house.

"Whatever is it?" Mother asked, starting to get up from her chair.

Herman's little face was red. He was breathless as he asked, "Ma, can I go down to the circus grounds with George and his friends? Can I, can I, can I? They're taking down the tents, and taking the animals off . . ."

"Yes, go on," Mother said, laughing at her young son's excitement. "But stay with George. And be back home before dark."

Mother couldn't help chuckling to herself as she heard Herman shouting. He was running as fast as he could to catch up with George.

"Boy, I can hardly wait!" Matt exclaimed. "They said they're going to take the whole circus across the Mohawk River bridge!"

"It ought to be lots of fun," George said, his blue eyes shining. He and his friends were strolling along as they waited for Herman, but they were impatient to get to the circus grounds.

"Will all the animals be in cages?" Herman asked breathlessly, as he caught up with the older boys. "Will they?"

"Oh most, I suppose," George said. "Come on, let's run. We want to see everything!"

"Oh, don't run," Herman groaned. "I just got here, and I'm out of breath."

George and Matt laughed at the little boy, whose heels were dragging as he tried to keep up with the big boys.

George rubbed his hand over Herman's tousled hair. "All right, Herman, we'll walk a little bit farther. But only till you catch your breath. We don't want to miss anything!"

"Hey, fellows, wait up," came a call from behind them. "What's your hurry?"

Richard turned around and yelled, "Come on, Will, we're going down to see the circus load up. They're going to take the whole circus across the bridge. Come along with us."

134

"What fun!" Will said as he caught up. "You should have seen the elephants last year!"

"Will there be elephants?" asked Herman joyfully. "They won't be in cages, will they?"

"They sure won't, Herman," Will laughed. "Come on though. Let's hurry."

The boys walked as fast as they could. They met more and more people walking toward the bridge. By the time they got there, quite a crowd had gathered to watch the procession.

"Oh, look at the elephants!" cried Herman. He pointed up the street leading to the bridge. There, in a single file, were the large grey elephants. Swinging and swaying they slowly lumbered up Washington Street toward the dark tunnel which was the bridge.

Suddenly something happened! A voice in the crowd screamed! The elephants stopped, and it looked as though they were going to topple back on each other!

George drew in his breath. It was frightening to watch them. What could be happening. The boys all started to run toward the excitement. Their curiosity outweighed their fear. Herman ran to George and slid his hand into George's.

The lead elephant threw his trunk over his head. His mouth opened as though he were laughing. Again the trainers, with their sticks and hooks, made the elephants get into a straight line and walk toward the opening of the bridge.

Obediently the elephants again ambled along. But just as the first elephant reached the opening of the bridge, he threw his trunk over his head and trumpeted loudly. The three elephants following stopped and swung around in huge, awkward turns. This time, though, the trainers could not get them to go back into their neat straight lines. One of the elephants plodded slowly down to the water under the bridge. The other elephants followed the leader.

"They don't like that bridge," whispered Matt.

A lady standing near the boys laughed. "They wouldn't cross the bridge last year, either."

"Oh, see what the elephants are doing!" Herman shouted. He pointed toward the elephants that were now down in the river.

By this time everyone was laughing. For there in the water, the elephants were frolicking and playing! They dipped their trunks into the water and sprayed it over their backs.

" You know those elephants are smart," a man behind George said to a friend. "They never forget. There are ghosts on that bridge!"

Richard, George, Matt, and Will looked at each other wisely. They knew about ghosts!

Nearly all eyes were on the elephants, who continued to play in the water. Suddenly Richard cried, "Look at the bridge!"

Matt, George, and Will wheeled around to look at the bridge opening.

"There's the ghost!" Richard whispered hoarsely. The boys were too frightened to run.

Herman was clinging to George's hand. The boys all stared with frightened fascination at the opening of the bridge. They could see something

138

moving in the shadows. Slowly a tall, dark, straight figure moved out from the shadows of the inside of the bridge.

George stood motionless as he watched. He couldn't move! His eyes almost hurt, he looked so hard. Slowly the figure came out into the pale evening light.

"Is that the ghost?" Matt cried. Then he started to laugh, making a funny, high, squeaky sound. "Why, that's Jim Cuff!"

George and Will stared in amazement at the Indian. Then they started laughing too. But Richard didn't laugh.

Jim Cuff walked toward the boys. His long straight face was very solemn, but his dark eyes had laughter in them as he asked, "Why you boys run from me on bridge?" Then he drew himself up proudly to his full height. "Jim Cuff is no ghost. Jim Cuff is the last of the mighty tribe of the Mohawks!"

The Boat on
the Erie Canal

THE BOYS laughed and laughed at their fright. How easy it was to imagine a ghost in such a dark ghostly place as the dim old bridge! Jim Cuff, with his long hair and his tall straight body, didn't look like other people. He didn't walk like other people either. He seemed to glide on his shoeless feet.

All the boys except Richard thought it was funny. He didn't laugh. Even that next winter at school, when Matt or Will made a funny remark about how they were fooled by the ghost, Richard would tighten his mouth and say nothing. He didn't like to talk about the ghost.

140

Richard did not like to be wrong. He wasn't wrong very often. He was the top scholar in the class. He always made one hundred in spelling and in history. He knew all the answers, even when the rest of the class didn't.

"Heard you saw your seven-foot ghost again, Richard," teased one of the boys.

"We sure did!" Matt answered for Richard, "and he talked to us this time!"

All the boys on the school ground laughed.

"He did look scary though, didn't he, Richard?" asked George. Richard's mouth was tight, and his face looked dark and sullen. He made no answer. George shrugged and walked off with some of the other boys.

During school hours though, Richard was in better humor. That is, until he and George had an argument about an arithmetic problem.

Miss Johnson called on Richard to put his example on the blackboard. Richard wrote out his figures in nice, clear numbers and drew a neat line under the answer.

George, who had watched him working the problem, raised his hand. "Miss Johnson, the answer should be 32,426 instead of his answer."

The teacher turned in her chair. "Very well, George, put your work on the board and we shall see. Now everyone check as George writes the figures, and see which answer is right."

George wrote his problem down very quickly. The figures weren't so neat, but the answer was right. George did understand numbers and liked to do arithmetic.

"You are right, George." Miss Johnson turned to the class. "Do you all understand?"

She waited for questions. When there weren't any, she said, "Then you may all put your work away. School is dismissed."

Richard's face was scarlet. He returned to his seat without looking at anyone.

142

Miss Johnson called George to her desk. "You do so well with your numbers and drawing, George, that I wish you would try a little harder with your spelling and writing." Then she smiled and asked, "What are you building now? Are you making anything new?"

Miss Johnson was always nice, even when she scolded. Her blue eyes were pretty and kind. With her fair clear skin and her smooth dark hair brushed back over her ears in a plump knot on the back of her head, George thought she looked as pretty as Elizabeth's dolls.

George was glad to have a chance to tell her what he was doing. Miss Johnson was the only teacher he knew whom he could really talk to.

"I am trying to make an engine which will make a propeller go around," George said.

"What are you going to do with it?" Miss Johnson asked with interest.

"Oh, I'm going to put it on my boat."

"Oh?" Then Miss Johnson asked, "Don't engines usually make a stroke back and forth, like the drivers on a locomotive which, in going back and forth, make the wheels go round?"

"That's right," George said seriously. "But I think an engine could power a round and round motion more efficiently."

"Are you working on this now, George?"

"Oh yes," he answered. "I plan to have it finished very soon. I'm going to try it out on the Erie Canal."

"Well, you just work at it. I am sure you can do it." Miss Johnson smiled kindly.

A FIGHT

While Miss Johnson and George were talking, Richard walked past.

George was still thinking about his engine and how he was going to make his boat work as he walked out into the school yard. He wasn't watching where he was walking. Suddenly he tripped. He almost fell into the dust! After scrambling to regain his footing, he saw Richard standing by him and smirking.

"What are you going to do with your big boat?" Richard taunted.

George looked at Richard and frowned. So it was Richard who had tripped him! George straightened his shoulders and clenched his fists. He didn't want to argue with Richard, though. He was in a hurry to get to the shop.

George set his mouth but answered quietly, "It isn't a big boat. It's only a small toy boat. I'm going to run it on the Erie Canal."

Richard smirked as he asked, "What makes you think it will run?"

"It will run," George replied in an even voice. He wanted to get away from Richard.

"Who says?" sneered Richard.

"I say!" George retorted, and he couldn't resist adding, "Miss Johnson does too!"

"Aw, the teacher's so dumb. She doesn't even know the right answer to an arithmetic problem!" shouted Richard.

That did it! George set his jaw. His face was white with anger. Richard had gone too far! He'd called Miss Johnson dumb! Richard was asking for a fight, and he was going to get it!

George flung his books on the ground. He crouched down a little and went into Richard, punching as hard as he could with both fists. Richard groaned a little as George's blows landed. Then he pushed George back and aimed a strong right fist as George's face.

"Hey, look! A fight!" yelled Joe.

"It's George and Richard!" cried Matt.

All the boys in the school yard gathered round. Some who had already started home came running back to see the excitement.

146

"Boy, that Richard has been asking for a fight," Matt exclaimed. "He was bound to get it! Come on, George, give it to him!"

Just then Richard landed a walloping blow on George's jaw. "Ouch!" cried Will. Just hearing that sound made him hurt. "Come on, George," he shouted. "Lay him out!"

George was breathing in short hard gasps and was sweating. His eyes were narrow blue slits. He leaped about, trying to get away from Richard's blows. Yet he tried to get close enough to get in some blows himself. With a yell, he jumped and knocked Richard down. Then he started to pound him with both fists.

"Boys! Boys!" cried Miss Johnson from the school door. She lifted her full skirts a little to run through the dusty school yard. "Oh my! Stop that at once!"

She hurried over to the two tussling boys rolling in the brown dust. She leaned down and

147

pulled George up by his collar. "Now get up, and both of you go on home! And stop this fighting right now. I'm ashamed of you!"

George stood up. He didn't even look at the teacher. He was still mad at Richard. He brushed off his pants a little, picked up his books and stood back to watch Richard. His shoulders heaved and his breath came in short gasps, and his pink face was streaked with mud from dust and perspiration.

Richard didn't look at George. He got to his feet, grabbed his books, and started off for home. Joe walked behind him.

Matt and Will came over to George. "Richard had that fight coming," Matt said. "Let's go."

Miss Johnson shook her head. Why on earth would boys want to get into such a fight! As the boys all walked off and the other spectators followed them, she turned and went back into the schoolhouse. She was still shaking her head.

There was no more fighting between George and Richard. Richard didn't say anything more to George, and George was too busy working on his boat to think about anything else.

Then came the day to try out the boat! Will and Matt came along with George to the Erie Canal to run the boat. A short distance behind, Joe and Richard followed to tease. They were sure the boat wouldn't run.

A BOAT THAT RAN

It was a glorious sunny afternoon in April of 1861. The air had just a touch of the feeling of a warm springtime. The boys were happy with thoughts of the summer to come. It was exciting, too, to see if the new boat would really run.

George ran on ahead. As they came closer to the canal, Matt asked, "Where are you going to put her in the water?"

"Right here," answered George. He knelt down on the grassy green bank and gently placed the boat in the water. Richard and Joe leaned up against a tree and watched quietly.

George stretched out flat on the grass and reached over to the boat.

"Can I help?" asked Will.

"No, I'll have it here in a minute," George answered as he placed everything so it would be ready. Then he started the engine.

"There she goes!" cried Matt.

Indeed the little boat did go, cutting right through the water! The engine chugged and the propeller went round and round, sending the little craft churning right through the water!

George crouched back on his heels. He took a deep breath and smiled broadly. What a wonderful thrill to have the boat really work!

Will and Matt jumped up and down as they screamed, "Look at her go! Look at her go!"

150

Richard and Joe were very much interested in watching the boat. George didn't notice, though. He was too busy watching it himself.

Suddenly the boat started to roll to its right side! "George! What's wrong?" cried Matt.

George leaped to his feet! The boat rolled on over. With its engine choking with water, it started to sink!

George jumped into the cold water of the canal and paddled hard to reach his boat.

Off to War

GEORGE'S WET HEAD soon bobbed up, and he headed for the bank with the boat in his arms. Matt and Will reached as far over the water as they dared to pull George onto the bank. George was breathless as he scrambled out of the water with the boat in his arms. He sat down heavily. Then he held the boat up to pour the water out.

"I'm sure glad you got the boat out!" exclaimed Matt. "Can you fix it to run again? Will it be all right now?"

George was looking at the boat carefully as he was thinking what would need to be done to fix it. "I think I can fix it," he answered slowly. He wrinkled his forehead as he thought. The engine was too strong for the boat. That was the reason she had gone over. He must make the boat heavier and he must slow down the engine. He'd have to get back to the shop. George never gave up. He always tried to think of a way to make things work the way he wanted them to.

George looked down at his wet clothes and at the very wet boat. His hair was dripping down his face, and his clothes were making a pool of water on the grass around him. He started to laugh a little. He looked so funny with his sopping wet boat on his lap. Matt and Will started to laugh too when they looked at George.

Slowly Richard and Joe walked over to the bank where George was sitting. Though they had broad grins, they didn't look unkind.

Richard came up to George and stooped down to look at the boat. "You were right, George," he said quietly. "It did run."

"It sure did run, but not for long!" George grinned at Richard.

"That really was something!" exclaimed Will. "Did you see her go!"

George went back to the shop, and he spent many hours fixing his boat. Mr. Westinghouse and George's brother John didn't know why George was spending so much time on a toy boat. He would work on it for a while. Then he would try it again on the canal. More times than not George had to jump in the water after the boat.

"George, why do you spend so much time with that foolish boat?" asked John.

George frowned. His boat wasn't foolish.

"I want an engine to make things go round and round. This one makes a propeller go around and makes the boat go through the water."

John shook his head and laughed. "What makes it go down in the water?"

"Aw!" George made a face.

It wasn't long before the boys were talking of a more serious matter. For this was the spring of 1861, and on April 12, 1861, the first shots were fired at Fort Sumter. Then the differences between the states flared into open war.

It didn't seem possible that here was a real war in our United States. Everyone was deeply troubled over these terrible events.

George's older brothers talked of enlisting in the northern forces. Mrs. Westinghouse's face was white and drawn as her sons, one after the other, talked of going off to war.

"Pa," said John, "I was talking to the recruiting officer, and I can sign up in the Navy."

"I would like to join the Volunteer Cavalry," Albert said.

"Boys," Father said seriously. "I would advise you to wait a little while before you enlist. This fighting will not last long."

156

Most people hoped and prayed that these differences between the North and the South would be settled soon.

John kept on talking to the recruiting officers, though, and he would talk to George about what they said. "I think we must enlist," John said. "It is our duty to fight for our country."

"I think so too," George agreed enthusiastically. "I think we should get this over quickly."

"Oh, I didn't mean you, George. You're too young. I think Albert and I should go." John saw George pull up straight and tall. George did look as big as a man. Though he was only fourteen, he was as tall as his brothers. John hadn't meant to hurt George's feelings. Quickly John added, "One of us has to stay at home to look after Ma and Pa and the girls."

"Herman can do that," said George.

"Oh, Herman is only eight. He can't do it," John said. "It will have to be you."

157

George was thinking. He looked at John. He was every bit as tall as John, and his shoulders were as broad. His eyes looked faraway as he thought, "I bet I could go to Albany and sign up. I bet they wouldn't even ask my age. The recruiters would be glad to sign me up!"

He started to smile. He thought about the battlefield, where they needed all those men. He could see the proud stars and stripes waving at the front of the line, and behind that, the battle flags. Maybe he could man a cannon with its mighty roar, or go running along in an advance and fall on his stomach to fire at the enemy.

He knew he must enlist. Then he thought about how he would do it. He would slip away some morning and board the train for Albany. He would be in uniform before John was!

The next day at school George was far away in his thoughts, planning his future. He could just see himself in soldier's blue.

"George! George!" Matt yelled at him. "For goodness sakes, answer me!"

George's blue eyes were wide when at last he realized Matt was talking to him. George decided he would have to tell Matt. What about Matt going along? That would be dandy! They could be soldiers together. "Matt," whispered George, "can you keep a secret?"

"Sure," Matt answered. "What?"

George looked about him to make sure no one was listening. "Matt, I'm going to join the army."

"What!" cried Matt.

"Shhh!" frowned George. "Would you like to go with me?"

Matt didn't say anything. He really didn't know whether he would or not.

"Listen!" George told him how they could take the morning train to Albany. They could be soldiers together. It wouldn't be for long. The war would be won, and they would be back home.

160

"What are you two whispering about?" Will asked as he joined them.

George looked up. Will would be a good one too. He was big, and he looked at least sixteen. So George told Will his plans.

GEORGE'S PLAN

The next morning the three boys gathered at the school gate. In excited whispers George made the plans. "We'll leave home early in the morning. Don't let anyone see you go. We can meet down by the train station."

"What are you fellows up to?"

George wheeled around, but it was only Joe, and behind him, Richard. George turned to his friends, and Matt and Will nodded. Why not ask Richard and Joe to come too?

"Come here. We'll tell you." George motioned to them to join his group.

161

The five boys stood in a close circle while George told Joe and Richard what they were going to do. All the boys were excited. They all talked at once of the wondrous thrill of joining up and fighting the war.

"All right, this is the plan," commanded the leader. "We'll go on Friday morning."

"This Friday?" asked Will. "I've already made plans to—"

George glared at Will. "Yes, this Friday. Get some clothes together into a carpetbag."

"I don't have a carpetbag," Joe said slowly. "I don't have any bag at all."

"Well, borrow one," George said in disgust. "Or tie your things in an old shirt or something. We'll meet down by the station. Get on the Albany train. We'll be safe as soon as it pulls out! Once we get to Albany, all we have to do is sign up. Then we'll be on our way. Before we know it we'll be fighting in a real battle."

"Do you think the recruiters will believe we're really old enough?"

"Of course they will. We're all as big as sixteen-year-olds."

"Well, I'm not as big as the rest of you," Richard said doubtfully.

George drew down the corners of his mouth as he looked at Richard. Up to this time Richard would have been ready to fight anyone who said he was smaller than the other boys.

"I don't know whether I can get out of the house without getting caught," Will said.

"Look, it's almost school time!" George said impatiently. "The day is Friday. We'll meet on the corner at Washington and State Streets." He was whispering now. "Come on, we've got to get into school, but remember!"

On Friday morning George lay awake, just waiting until it was time to get up. Finally the rays of sunlight peeked through his window and he could hear his mother and father downstairs as the family gathered for breakfast. Quickly he gathered a few of his clothes and stuffed them into an old carpetbag. He pushed the carpetbag as far under his bed as he could until after breakfast.

George ate his breakfast as quickly as he could, without saying very much to anyone. He didn't want any member of the family to guess his plans. He smiled to himself. Wouldn't they be surprised when he wrote them!

He ran back upstairs to his bed, pulled his carpetbag out, put his coat over it, and held his cap in his hand. He paused and listened. The house sounded quiet. If he could only get down the stairs and out the back door!

He listened at his door. Then he ran down the stairs as softly as he could. Annie, the house-maid, was in the kitchen, but she was over by the stove with her back to him. He could hear his mother in the front room talking to Herman. He waited for an instant. Then he rushed through the kitchen and out the back door. He closed the door so quietly Annie didn't even turn. She never knew he went past!

He grinned as he ducked out behind the barn to the alley. He ran down to the end of the alley. Then he hesitated just long enough to put his jacket on and jam his cap on his head. He looked about him. There wasn't a soul!

The early morning air was refreshing. The pale morning sunlight came down in shafts over the housetops. The whole morning felt exciting!

He ran through the alleys and down the back streets. When he crossed a main street, he would stop carefully to see if anyone was out. Then he would dash to the next back street.

Matt was waiting for him at their meeting place. "Do you think we ought to, really, George?" Matt looked a little worried.

165

"Of course, Matt," George answered confidently. He smiled broadly as he looked around. "Where are the others?"

There was no one in sight. Matt shook his head. "I don't think they're coming."

"Not coming!" George snorted. "Why not?"

"I don't think they are." Matt frowned. He wasn't really sure he ought to have come.

"Well, come on then." George grabbed Matt's arm. "Let's get on the train."

They climbed aboard the train and quickly found a seat. They both slipped down in it as far as they could. They didn't want anyone to recognize them, especially before the train started.

"What will we do if we see someone we know?" Matt asked fearfully.

"It isn't that! It's what if someone we know sees us!" answered George. "They won't expect us to be here. Just keep looking toward the window, and keep your cap down as far as you can."

166

A Hasty Return

Mrs. Westinghouse went out to the kitchen to help Annie do up the breakfast work. Suddenly she put her hand up to her forehead.

"Oh, Annie, I just remembered the dressmaker is coming today, and the material I ordered is still at Barney's Dry Goods Store." She paused for only a moment. "I know. I'll send George for it. Have you seen him?"

Annie looked around. "No, I haven't. Maybe he went back up to his room."

"George!" his mother called, going to the stairway. When there was no answer, she cupped her hand around her mouth and called louder.

167

"Did he go on to school?" Annie asked.

"Well, I think not yet, but I'm not sure." She went through the house. There were his books in their book strap, just where he had tossed them the afternoon before. She opened the front door and looked out. There was no sight of George.

She went back through the house. Where could the boy be! She opened the back door. He was probably out in the barn working.

"George! George!" She was shouting now.

"Do you want me, Ma?" Herman asked.

Mrs. Westinghouse looked puzzled. "No, Herman, but do you know where your brother George is? I want him to do an errand for me."

Herman shook his head. "Guess he's gone on to school. Can I do the errand?"

"No, Herman, you go to school. I want George to bring some material from the dry goods store. It will be quite heavy. But now I would just like to know where he is!"

Just then Mrs. Matthews, a neighbor, called from near the front door, "Mrs. Westinghouse! Mrs. Westinghouse!"

Mrs. Westinghouse lifted her skirts as she ran back to the front door. "What is it?" she asked breathlessly.

"My Mary said she saw George early this morning. He was running down the alley with a carpetbag," Mrs. Matthews answered.

"A carpetbag in his hand!" George's mother sank into a chair. "Do sit down, Mrs. Matthews," she said and gestured to the settee.

"Yes," Mrs. Matthews nodded. "Mary said he seemed to be trying to keep from being seen. He kept in the shadows and behind the barns!"

"Are you sure it was my George?" asked the shocked mother, sitting down abruptly.

"There is no doubt!" She clucked her tongue. "One of the neighbor boys said George has been talking about running away to go to war."

170

George's mother pursed her mouth for an instant. Then she rose and called, "Annie, please take this message to Mr. Westinghouse."

Annie ran to take off her apron and get her shawl. Mrs. Westinghouse hastily wrote a note to her husband, telling him about George.

Annie ran into the shop and handed the note to Mr. Westinghouse. His calm face didn't show any signs of upset at the news. He glanced at the clock, reached for his hat, and left.

ALL ABOARD

George and Matt were feeling very uneasy. It seemed as if the train would never start. They did not see any of their neighbors, but they were relieved when the conductor finally called, "All aboard!" and climbed into the car where George and Matt were sitting. He started to pull the bell rope to signal the train to start.

171

George took a deep breath and let it out with a sigh of relief. But his relief was too soon! A man of important bearing got on the car right behind the conductor. His face looked serious. "Wait," he commanded with authority.

Everyone in the car turned to see who this was and what he was doing! George didn't need to turn. He recognized the voice.

Mr. Westinghouse went striding through the car looking from left to right on either side of the aisle. George felt a deep heaviness in the center of his stomach. His throat felt tight and prickly. He looked up to see his father standing squarely in front of him. George looked at Matt whose face was very red. Both boys would have liked to slip right back through the seat, where they would never be seen again!

"George, I guess you'd better come back home." Mr. Westinghouse's voice was quiet. He didn't sound at all excited.

George and Matt stood up. George's father didn't look angry. He didn't even raise his voice when he spoke to them.

The two boys followed Mr. Westinghouse off the train. They didn't look at each other as they walked home. Matt felt a little relieved that he hadn't had to go through with running off to war. But George felt a sad twinge as he heard the train whistle and the chugging of the locomotive. He was sorry the train had started off to Albany without him.

A Train Wreck

George went home and left his carpetbag. Then he picked up his books and went off to school. George and Matt got tardy marks when they went into the schoolroom. As they slid into their seats, the other boys stared at them and did a lot of whispering.

When he came home for lunch Mother kissed him, but she didn't say anything about the events of the morning. The family gathering at the lunch table was just as though nothing had happened. George was relieved because no one said anything about his trip. By the time lunch was over George felt better about all of it.

As George and his father were leaving the house together, Mr. Westinghouse turned to his son and said quietly, "George, you will be free to go to war when you are really old enough. I hope, though, that the fighting will be over long before then."

George turned his thoughts back to his work at the shop. He was so interested in making a rotary engine that he devoted almost all his time to it. This steam engine was based on the idea he had first tried on his little boat. He built the steam engine which was a successful rotary engine when he was only fifteen years old. He received his first patent on this engine.

By the spring of 1863, when George was nearly seventeen years old, it was all too evident that the War between the States was not to be settled quickly. John and Albert had joined up and gone off to war. John was in the Navy and Albert in the Volunteer Cavalry.

"Father, don't you think I ought to join up now?" George asked. "The news from the front makes it look as if Lee's army might break through into Pennsylvania. Pa, I really think it's time I signed up!"

Mr. Westinghouse frowned, but he had to agree with George. "Perhaps you are right, son."

George was eager to go. He signed up first in the Army. He tried to recruit fifty men to form a company. He went back to Central Bridge, but most of the men had already gone. He asked about his old friend Jacob.

"Jacob signed up last summer, and he's already at the front," he was told.

For all his searching he was able to find only seventeen men to sign up with him. George served in the Army until December, 1864. Then, on the basis of his good military record and by passing an examination with a very high grade, he was appointed an Acting Third Assistant

178

Engineer in the Navy. He served on the ship "Muscoota" and later on the "Stars and Stripes."

George came home in the summer of 1865, after the war was ended. His brother John didn't get home until fall. George found his parents saddened by the deaths of two of his sisters, and his brother Albert, who had been killed in battle at McLeod's Mills, Louisiana.

Twelve-year-old Herman was happy to have George home again. It had been a very sad and lonesome time during the years of war. Herman felt proud when he looked at George. He thought George was very straight and tall.

George enrolled at Union College in Schenectady as a sophomore that fall. With his head held high he would stride along briskly through the trees on his way to classes. He did well in his geometry class, but in his French and English classes he passed the time drawing locomotives and engines on his shirt cuffs!

Though George had grown up, his thoughts still were not on his studies. He wanted to work out his own ideas, not just sit and listen!

He soon left college to go to work in his father's shop. He worked again on his rotary engine and obtained a patent on it. His eyes grew brighter, and his cheeks regained their old glow as he worked at his bench.

CAR REPLACERS FOR RAILROADS

Sometimes George would take trips to other towns to take care of business for his father. One day when George was on the train going to Albany, the train stopped suddenly.

The conductor soon came through and announced, "We will be held up here for a short time. The train ahead of us has two cars off the track. We will have to wait until the crew gets them back on the track.

The short time became a long time. George and some of the other passengers got off the train and walked down the track to see the derailed train. The railroad crew of men were working hard to lift the cars back on the track.

George walked around the cars. He drew his eyebrows together for a moment. "This is unnecessary!" he exclaimed. "The whole job could be done in fifteen minutes if they had only clamped side rails at an angle to the main track and extended them to the derailed cars. Then the engine could have pulled them back on the track very easily." George was talking aloud as if he were talking to himself. "All railroads should have car replacers for accidents like this."

A man standing next to him retorted unkindly, "Why don't you tell the railroads?"

"I guess I will," George answered.

As George always did when he decided something was needed, he started to think about how he could make a car replacer. He made plans for railroad car replacers before he went to bed that very night! He found some men who were willing to put up the necessary money to manufacture the replacers. Very soon George Westinghouse was selling the replacers to the railroads.

The most famous of George Westinghouse's inventions came about as the result of another train wreck. George was on a train going to Troy, New York, when suddenly the train stopped with a jolt. George was almost thrown from his seat. The passengers tried to get back on their seats and were picking up their belongings which had been thrown to the floor.

"What happened?" demanded a man who was sitting close to the door.

"It's all right, folks," the conductor said. "We had to stop because there has been a serious collision ahead."

"What happened?" asked a lady excitedly.

"Two freight trains had a head-on collision, the conductor replied.

George and his fellow passengers walked up to look at the trouble. The freight cars were toppled off the tracks at all kinds of peculiar angles. Cars were crushed into tangled hunks of metal. Machinery, clothing, and food, the cargo from the freight cars, were strewn all over the tracks! It would cost thousands of dollars to repair and replace all the damage.

"How did it happen?" George asked. He was horrified at all the wreckage.

"The engineer of the second train saw the freight train ahead of him," answered a man who was standing nearby, "but he just couldn't stop."

"What do you mean, he couldn't stop!" demanded George. "Why couldn't he stop?"

"You just can't stop a heavy freight train in seconds!" the man replied.

Stopping a Train

GEORGE WESTINGHOUSE set about to invent a brake which would stop a heavy train in seconds! He thought of nothing else while he tried to work out a plan for a brake. He worked at his bench and tried to put together a model of a brake which would stop a train. How could trains go fast when they couldn't be stopped?

Finally he built a mechanical model of a brake system. Then he tried to think of a way to power it. The first thing he thought of was steam. Steam could force its way through and make the mechanical brake work. He frowned and shook his head. No, steam could not work.

184

The steam would have to go the entire length of the train. In winter it would get cold and become water with no power. George could think of nothing which could be used successfully.

One day a young lady sold George a subscription to a new magazine, *The Living Age*. In the first issue he read an article which gave him an idea for his air brake.

This article told of the difficulties a group of engineers had in digging a seven-mile tunnel through the Alps on the French-Italian border. Two crews of workmen, trying to chop and dig through the mountain, would take nearly fifty years to meet in the middle. These engineers had solved their problem by using compressed air to run their machinery!

George leaped to his feet. This was his answer! Compressed air! Compressed air could be sent the length of a train to set brakes on the wheels of the very last car!

George was excited as he built his model of the first air brake and found that it worked. Then he had to test it on a railroad train.

He talked to many railroad men, but none of them would believe that George's air brake would stop a train. Finally Mr. W. W. Card, a superintendent of the Panhandle Railroad, was impressed with George's brake. He persuaded the Board of Directors of his railroad to test the brake on one of their trains.

THE TRIAL RUN

The trial run was held on a beautiful sunshiny morning. When the locomotive, pulling its tender and four coaches pulled out of the station in Pittsburgh, the officials of the railroad and George were aboard for this most important ride.

Every car had a Westinghouse air brake, which was to be tested after several miles.

The engineer quickly got the locomotive up to a speed of 30 miles per hour. Suddenly a wagon drawn by a team of heavy horses pulled on to a crossing. Then the cartman saw the huge locomotive charging at him. He whipped his horses and shouted to get them across the track.

One of the large horses, frightened by the noise and whipping, reared up on its hind legs. It pulled its teammate back with it. The driver screamed as the locomotive hurtled onward.

The engineer was horrified at the sight on the track ahead of him. He pulled at the new brake lever with all his might. The brakes set on the wheels, and the train lurched to a stop only four feet from the terrified cartman. Never had a train been stopped so quickly!

The officials who had been thrown from their seats by the sudden stop came rushing up. "What on earth is the matter?" Another demanded, "What are you trying to do?"

They soon saw what had happened and realized the great benefit the air brake would bring to railroad transportation.

Soon after this thrilling ride a group of railroad men met with George Westinghouse to organize the Westinghouse Air Brake Company. George was named President of this new company formed to manufacture the air brake. He was not quite twenty-three years old.

GEORGE WESTINGHOUSE'S WORK

"If someday they can say of me that in my work I have contributed something to the welfare and happiness of my fellow men, I shall be satisfied," George Westinghouse once said.

There are few men who have done as much for their fellow men as George Westinghouse. He made two very important contributions to our way of life. He advanced transportation by the invention and development of the air brake. He advanced the manufacture of power by introducing alternating current in electricity.

When George Westinghouse saw anything that he thought he could improve, he started to work on it. He usually found a way. He invented many useful things. Then he manufactured them so that people could use them.

During his lifetime he obtained 361 patents. In 1856, when he was nineteen years old, he received his first patent for the rotary steam engine. He had invented this engine when he was fifteen. He averaged a patent every six weeks for the rest of his life.

In addition to inventing the replacer to get derailed trains back on the track and the air brake for stopping trains, he invented a new system for signals and switches for railroads. He found a way to make natural gas go through pipes and made a meter to measure the flow of gas.

George Westinghouse saw a demonstration of Edison's incandescent lamp and discovered that electricity could be sent over only a few miles at low voltages.

He searched for a way to transmit electricity at high voltages and to step it down to low pressures where it was to be used. He heard of an invention in Europe which could do this. He bought the patent, only to find it would not work. Within three weeks after receiving the mechanism he perfected an efficient transformer. This transformer made the use of alternating current possible. By means of alternating current, electricity could be brought to every farm and village, as well as to the cities.

George organized a company to build the transformers. He received the contract to light the World's Fair of 1893 in Chicago. People gazed in wonder at the beautiful buildings, brilliantly lighted by this new method.

That same year The Westinghouse Machine Company was organized to build high speed engines designed by George's brother Herman.

Besides all the wonderful inventions George Westinghouse developed and manufactured, he was known for his kindness and fairness to the many employees of his companies. As he had said he would, he gave his employees a half-holiday on Saturdays. This was the first step to the five-day week. In 1908 he established a pension plan for employees. In 1913 he started the policy of paid vacations for employees.

On December 1, 1957, the name of George Westinghouse was added to The Hall of Fame for Great Americans at New York University. Former President Herbert Hoover was the main speaker at the ceremony honoring the life of this man, who was born in a small town in the United States, and through his own efforts and great deeds was known around the world.

More About This Book

WHEN GEORGE WESTINGHOUSE LIVED

1846   GEORGE WESTINGHOUSE WAS BORN AT CENTRAL BRIDGE, NEW YORK, OCTOBER 6.

There were twenty-eight states in the Union.

James K. Polk was President.

The population of the country was about 21,345,000.

1846–
1856   GEORGE LIVED WITH HIS FAMILY IN CENTRAL BRIDGE, NEW YORK.

The Mexican War was fought, 1846-1848.

Gold was discovered in California, 1848.

Harriet Beecher Stowe's *Uncle Tom's Cabin* was published, 1852.

1856–
1863   GEORGE LIVED AND WENT TO SCHOOL IN SCHENECTADY, NEW YORK.

The Lincoln-Douglas debates were held, 1858.

The War between the States was fought, 1861-1865.

The Emancipation Proclamation was issued, 1863.

1863– WESTINGHOUSE SERVED IN WAR BETWEEN THE
1869   STATES AND LATER CONTINUED TO WORK ON
       INVENTIONS.

President Abraham Lincoln was assassinated, 1865.

The fisrt transatlantic cable was laid, 1866.

The first transcontinental railroad was completed, 1869.

1869– WESTINGHOUSE HEADED COMPANY FOR MANU-
1882   FACTURING AIR BRAKES AND OTHER DEVICES
       FOR RAILROADS.

Alexander G. Bell invented the telephone, 1876.

Thomas Edison invented the phonograph, 1878, and the electric light bulb, 1879.

James A. Garfield became President and was assassinated, 1881.

1882– WESTINGHOUSE ORGANIZED COMPANIES TO
1914   MANUFACTURE ELECTRICAL EQUIPMENT AND
       OTHER PRODUCTS.

The American Federation of Labor was organized, 1886.

The Spanish-American War was fought, 1898.

Wilbur and Orville Wright flew the first heavier-than-air aircraft, 1903.

194

1914   GEORGE WESTINGHOUSE DIED MARCH 12 IN
         NEW YORK CITY.

There were forty-eight states in the Union.

Woodrow Wilson was President.

The population of the country was about
97,465,000.

DO YOU REMEMBER?

1. Why did George miss school on the April morning
   when the story begins?

2. What work did George's father do, and why was
   George proud of him?

3. How did George and Jacob help to thresh grain
   on Farmer Vroman's farm?

4. Why did Mr. Westinghouse and his family move
   to Schenectady, New York?

5. How did George and Matt Schroder meet and
   become friends?

6. What exciting things did George find to see and
   do in Schenectady?

7. Why did Mr. Westinghouse object to George making toys in the workshop?

8. How did George get a workbench and tools to use in making things?

9. What agreement did Mr. Westinghouse make with George for working in the shop?

10. What device did George make for cutting pipe into short lengths for his father?

11. What kind of engine did George make to run his toy boat?

12. What happened when George and Matt tried to run away to enlist in the army?

13. How did young Westinghouse manage to get his compressed air brakes tested?

14. What company was founded, with Westinghouse as president, to build air brakes?

15. What are some of George Westinghouse's most important inventions?

IT'S FUN TO LOOK UP THESE THINGS

1. What is a patent, and why is it important for inventors to get patents?

2. Why were threshing machines once widely used in farm sections of our country?

3. How does a rotary steam engine work differently from an ordinary steam engine?

4. Why have compressed air brakes been especially helpful to railroads?

5. What is a transformer, and how does it help in using electricity?

6. What is the Hall of Fame, where Westinghouse is honored for being a great American?

INTERESTING THINGS YOU CAN DO

1. Collect several pictures of covered bridges similar to the one mentioned in the story.

2. Find out how people have threshed grain from ancient times down to the present.

3. Make a list of Westinghouse's most important and successful inventions.

4. Read to find out what contributions Westinghouse made in the field of electricity.

5. What is an engineer, and why is Westinghouse referred to as an engineer?

6. Write a report on the subject, "How Westinghouse Helped People to Live Better."

OTHER BOOKS YOU MAY ENJOY READING

All about Famous Inventors and Their Inventions, Fletcher Pratt. Random House.

Boy and a Battery, A, Raymond F. Yates. Harper.

Energy and Power, Robert Irving. Knopf.

Exploring Science, Jonathan N. Leonard. World.

First Book of Science Experiments, Rose Wyler. Franklin Watts.

George Westinghouse, Henry Thomas. Putnam.

101 Science Experiments, Illa Podendorf. Grosset.

Story of Electricity, The, Mae and Ira Freeman. Random House.

INTERESTING WORDS IN THIS BOOK

acquaintance (ă kwän′tăns) : person merely known, not a close friend

alternating current (ôl′tĕr nāt′ĭng kûr′ĕnt) : electrical current that regularly and repeatedly changes its direction

amazement (ȧ māz′mĕnt) : great surprise

architect (är′kĭ tĕkt) : person who designs and oversees the construction of buildings

automatically (ô tổ măt′ĭ kăl ĭ) : self-moving or self-acting

barge (bärj) : large flat-bottomed boat, used for carrying freight or passengers

carpetbag (kär′pĕt băg′) : traveling bag or satchel made out of carpet

cobblestones (kŏb″l stōnz) : small, rounded stones formerly used for paving streets

compressed (kŏm prĕst′) : pressed together very closely

contraption (kŏn trăp′shŭn) : gadget

cradler (krā′dlẽr) : person who mows grain with a cradle

contribute (kŏn trĭb′ŭt) : provide something

defiant (dẽ fī′ănt) : bold

diligently (dĭl′ĭ gĕnt lĭ) : carefully, attentively

disappointment (dĭs ă point′mĕnt) : feeling a person has when something fails to come up to his hope or expectation

dismay (dĭs mā′) : alarm, feeling of fear that something may happen

excitement (ĕk sīt′mĕnt) : something which stirs up the feelings

enormous (ê nôr′mŭs) : exceedingly large

ferment (fĕr mĕnt′) : become sour or alcoholic by kind of chemical action

floe (flō) : chunk of floating ice

hesitate (hĕz ĭ tāt′) : pause or wait because of uncertainty of what to do

interrupt (ĭn′tĕ rŭpt′) : break in on, hinder

opportunity (ŏp′ŏr tū′nĭ tĭ) : good chance

perplex (pĕr plĕks′) : puzzle

propeller (prȯ pĕl′ĕr) : revolving shaft with blades, used to move something forward

quirk (kwûrk) : sudden turn or twist

spectator (spĕk tā′tĕr) : person who looks on without taking part

thresher (thrĕsh′ēr) : machine used to separate grain from the rest of a plant

thrifty (thrĭf′tĭ) : careful in spending

tollkeeper (tōl′kēp′ēr) : person who collects money from persons using certain roads or bridges

transformer (trăns fôr′mēr) : device used to step down or to step up current

voltage (vōl′tĭj) : means of measuring the strength of an electrical current

Childhood

OF FAMOUS AMERICANS

COLONIAL DAYS

JAMES OGLETHORPE, *Parks*
JOHN ALDEN, *Burt*
MYLES STANDISH, *Stevenson*
PETER STUYVESANT, *Widdemer*
POCAHONTAS, *Seymour*
PONTIAC, *Peckham*
SQUANTO, *Stevenson*
VIRGINIA DARE, *Stevenson*
WILLIAM BRADFORD, *Smith*
WILLIAM PENN, *Mason*

STRUGGLE for INDEPENDENCE

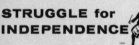

ANTHONY WAYNE, *Stevenson*
BEN FRANKLIN, *Stevenson*
BETSY ROSS, *Weil*
DAN MORGAN, *Bryant*
ETHAN ALLEN, *Winders*
FRANCIS MARION, *Steele*
GEORGE ROGERS CLARK, *Wilkie*
GEORGE WASHINGTON, *Stevenson*
ISRAEL PUTNAM, *Stevenson*
JOHN HANCOCK, *Cleven*
JOHN PAUL JONES, *Snow*
MARTHA WASHINGTON, *Wagoner*
MOLLY PITCHER, *Stevenson*
NATHAN HALE, *Stevenson*
NATHANAEL GREENE, *Peckham*
PATRICK HENRY, *Barton*
PAUL REVERE, *Stevenson*
TOM JEFFERSON, *Monsell*

EARLY NATIONAL GROWTH

ABIGAIL ADAMS, *Wagoner*
ALEC HAMILTON, *Higgins*
ANDY JACKSON, *Stevenson*
DAN WEBSTER, *Smith*
DeWITT CLINTON, *Widdemer*
DOLLY MADISON, *Monsell*
ELI WHITNEY, *Snow*
ELIAS HOWE, *Corcoran*
FRANCIS SCOTT KEY, *Stevenson*
HENRY CLAY, *Monsell*
JAMES FENIMORE COOPER, *Winders*
JAMES MONROE, *Widdemer*
JOHN AUDUBON, *Mason*
JOHN F. KENNEDY, *Frisbee*
JOHN JACOB ASTOR, *Anderson*
JOHN MARSHALL, *Monsell*
JOHN QUINCY ADAMS, *Weil*
LUCRETIA MOTT, *Burnett*
MATTHEW CALBRAITH PERRY, *Scharbach*
NANCY HANKS, *Stevenson*
NOAH WEBSTER, *Higgins*
OLIVER HAZARD PERRY, *Long*
RACHEL JACKSON, *Govan*
ROBERT FULTON, *Henry*
SAMUEL MORSE, *Snow*
SEQUOYAH, *Snow*
STEPHEN DECATUR, *Smith*
STEPHEN FOSTER, *Higgins*
WASHINGTON IRVING, *Widdemer*
ZACK TAYLOR, *Wilkie*

WESTWARD MOVEMENT

BRIGHAM YOUNG, *Jordan and Frisbee*
BUFFALO BILL, *Stevenson*
DANIEL BOONE, *Stevenson*
DAVY CROCKETT, *Parks*
GAIL BORDEN, *Paradis*
JED SMITH, *Burt*
JESSIE FREMONT, *Wagoner*